play guitar with...
the 90's

GW00646246

Wise Publications
London/New York/Paris/Sydney/Copenhagen/Madrid

Music Sales Limited
8-9 Frith Street,
London W1V 5TZ, England.
Music Sales Pty Limited
120 Rothschild Avenue,
Rosebery, NSW 2018, Australia.

Order No. AM957770
ISBN 0-7119-7879-4
This book © Copyright 1999
by Wise Publications

Music compiled and arranged by Arthur Dick
Music processed by Andrew Shiels
Cover photographs courtesy of
London Features International

Printed in the United Kingdom by
Caligraving Limited, Thetford, Norfolk.

CD programmed by John Moores
Recorded by Kester Sims
Guitar preparation by Charlie Chandler at Chandler Guitars
All guitars by Arthur Dick
With special thanks to Andy Milner at *Marshall* for supply of amplification

Your Guarantee of Quality
As publishers, we strive to produce
every book to the highest commercial standards.
The music has been freshly engraved and the book has
been carefully designed to minimise awkward page turns
and to make playing from it a real pleasure.
Particular care has been given to specifying acid-free,
neutral-sized paper made from pulps which have not been
elemental chlorine bleached. This pulp is from farmed
sustainable forests and was produced with
special regard for the environment.
Throughout, the printing and binding have been planned
to ensure a sturdy, attractive publication which
should give years of enjoyment.
If your copy fails to meet our high standards,
please inform us and we will gladly replace it.

www.playguitarwith.com

Music Sales' complete catalogue describes thousands of titles
and is available in full colour sections by subject, direct from
Music Sales Limited. Please state your areas of interest
and send a cheque/postal order for £1.50 for postage to:
Music Sales Limited, Newmarket Road,
Bury St. Edmunds, Suffolk IP33 3YB.

guitar tablature explained

Guitar music can be notated three different ways: on a musical stave, in tablature, and in rhythm slashes

RHYTHM SLASHES are written above the stave. Strum chords in the rhythm indicated. Round noteheads indicate single notes.

THE MUSICAL STAVE shows pitches and rhythms and is divided by lines into bars. Pitches are named after the first seven letters of the alphabet.

TABLATURE graphically represents the guitar fingerboard. Each horizontal line represents a string, and each number represents a fret.

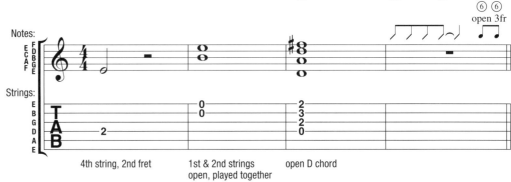

4th string, 2nd fret

1st & 2nd strings open, played together

open D chord

definitions for special guitar notation

SEMI-TONE BEND: Strike the note and bend up a semi-tone (1/2 step).

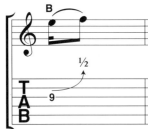

WHOLE-TONE BEND: Strike the note and bend up a whole-tone (whole step).

GRACE NOTE BEND: Strike the note and bend as indicated. Play the first note as quickly as possible.

QUARTER-TONE BEND: Strike the note and bend up a 1/4 step.

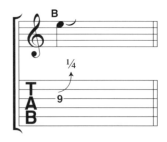

BEND & RELEASE: Strike the note and bend up as indicated, then release back to the original note.

COMPOUND BEND & RELEASE: Strike the note and bend up and down in the rhythm indicated.

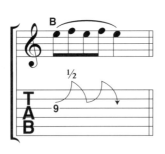

PRE-BEND: Bend the note as indicated, then strike it.

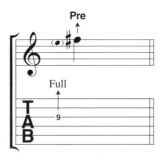

PRE-BEND & RELEASE: Bend the note as indicated. Strike it and release the note back to the original pitch.

UNISON BEND: Strike the two notes simultaneously and bend the lower note up to the pitch of the higher.

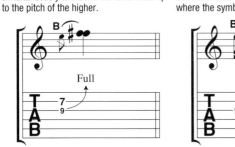

BEND & RESTRIKE: Strike the note and bend as indicated then restrike the string where the symbol occurs.

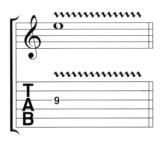

BEND, HOLD AND RELEASE: Same as bend and release but hold the bend for the duration of the tie.

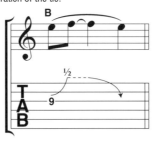

BEND AND TAP: Bend the note as indicated and tap the higher fret while still holding the bend.

VIBRATO: The string is vibrated by rapidly bending and releasing the note with the fretting hand.

HAMMER-ON: Strike the first (lower) note with one finger, then sound the higher note (on the same string) with another finger by fretting it without picking.

PULL-OFF: Place both fingers on the notes to be sounded, Strike the first note and without picking, pull the finger off to sound the second (lower) note.

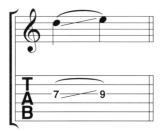

LEGATO SLIDE (GLISS): Strike the first note and then slide the same fret-hand finger up or down to the second note. The second note is not struck.

NOTE: The speed of any bend is indicated by the music notation and tempo.

4

SHIFT SLIDE (GLISS & RESTRIKE): Same as legato slide, except the second note is struck.

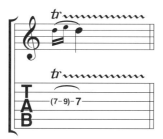

TRILL: Very rapidly alternate between the notes indicated by continuously hammering on and pulling off.

TAPPING: Hammer ("tap") the fret indicated with the pick-hand index or middle finger and pull off to the note fretted by the fret hand.

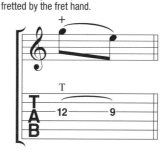

PICK SCRAPE: The edge of the pick is rubbed down (or up) the string, producing a scratchy sound.

MUFFLED STRINGS: A percussive sound is produced by laying the fret hand across the string(s) without depressing, and striking them with the pick hand.

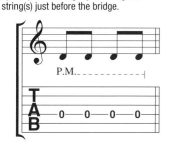

NATURAL HARMONIC: Strike the note while the fret-hand lightly touches the string directly over the fret indicated.

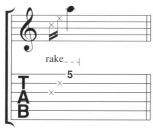

Harm.

PINCH HARMONIC: The note is fretted normally and a harmonic is produced by adding the edge of the thumb or the tip of the index finger of the pick hand to the normal pick attack.

P.H.

HARP HARMONIC: The note is fretted normally and a harmonic is produced by gently resting the pick hand's index finger directly above the indicated fret (in parentheses) while the pick hand's thumb or pick assists by plucking the appropriate string.

H.H.

PALM MUTING: The note is partially muted by the pick hand lightly touching the string(s) just before the bridge.

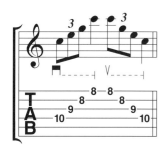

P.M.

RAKE: Drag the pick across the strings indicated with a single motion.

rake

TREMOLO PICKING: The note is picked as rapidly and continuously as possible.

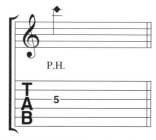

ARPEGGIATE: Play the notes of the chord indicated by quickly rolling them from bottom to top.

SWEEP PICKING: Rhythmic downstroke and/or upstroke motion across the strings.

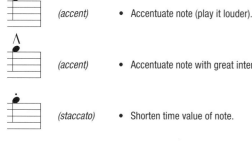

VIBRATO DIVE BAR AND RETURN: The pitch of the note or chord is dropped a specific number of steps (in rhythm) then returned to the original pitch.

w/bar

VIBRATO BAR SCOOP: Depress the bar just before striking the note, then quickly release the bar.

w/bar

VIBRATO BAR DIP: Strike the note and then immediately drop a specific number of steps, then release back to the original pitch.

w/bar

additional musical definitions

> (accent) • Accentuate note (play it louder).

(accent) • Accentuate note with great intensity.

(staccato) • Shorten time value of note.

• Downstroke

V • Upstroke

D.%. al Coda

D.C. al Fine

tacet

• Go back to the sign (%), then play until the bar marked *To Coda* ⊕ then skip to the section marked ⊕ *Coda*.

• Go back to the beginning of the song and play until the bar marked *Fine* (end).

• Instrument is silent (drops out).

• Repeat bars between signs.

|1.| |2.|

• When a repeated section has different endings, play the first ending only the first time and the second ending only the second time.

NOTE: Tablature numbers in parentheses mean: 1. The note is sustained, but a new articulation (such as hammer on or slide) begins.
2. A note may be fretted but not necessarily played.

common people

Music by Pulp. Lyrics by Jarvis Cocker

Intro

2 bar count in:

Verse

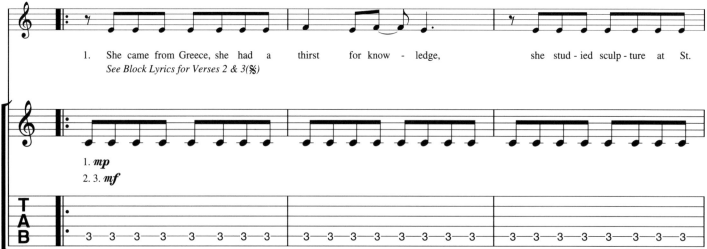

1. She came from Greece, she had a thirst for know - ledge, she stud - ied sculp - ture at St.
See Block Lyrics for Verses 2 & 3(%)

1. *mp*
2. 3. *mf*

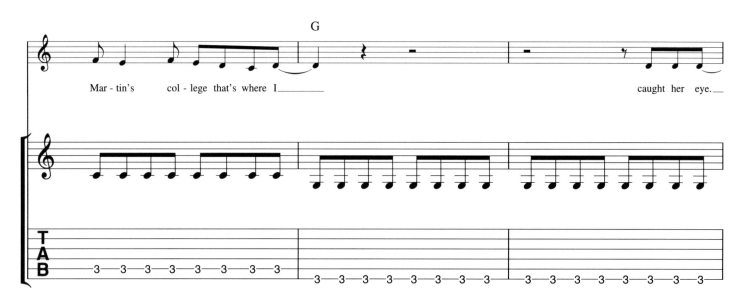

Mar - tin's col - lege that's where I_____ caught her eye._____

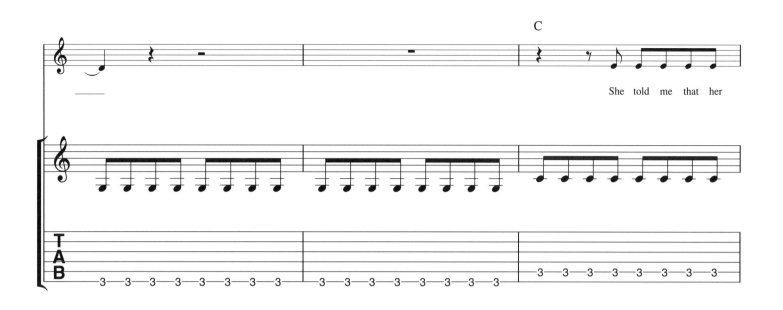

She told me that her

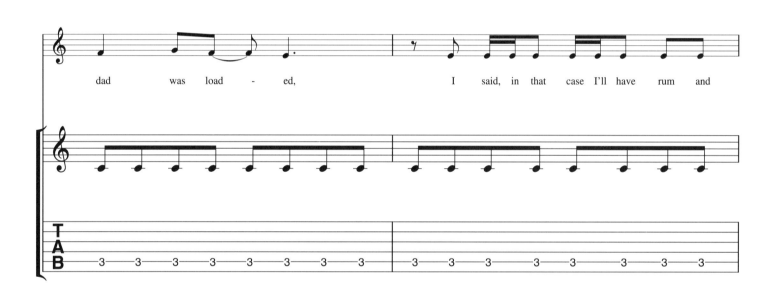

dad was load - ed, I said, in that case I'll have rum and

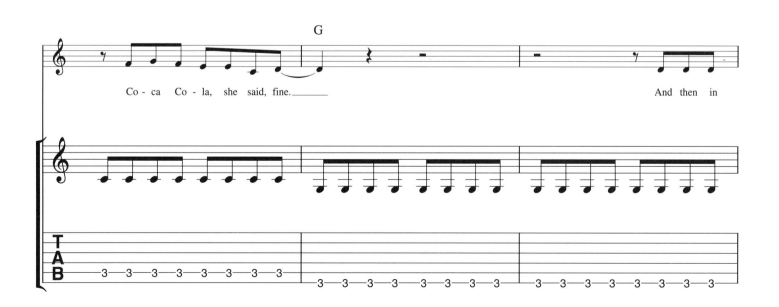

Co - ca Co - la, she said, fine.___ And then in

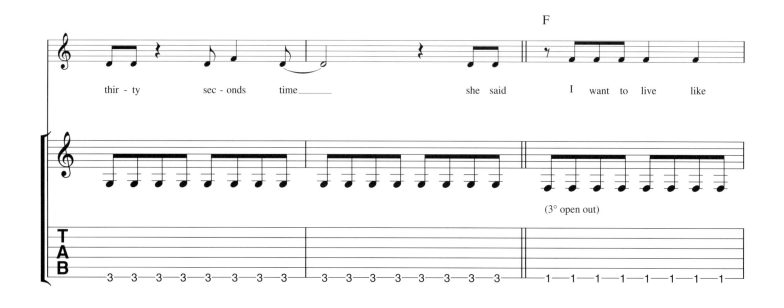

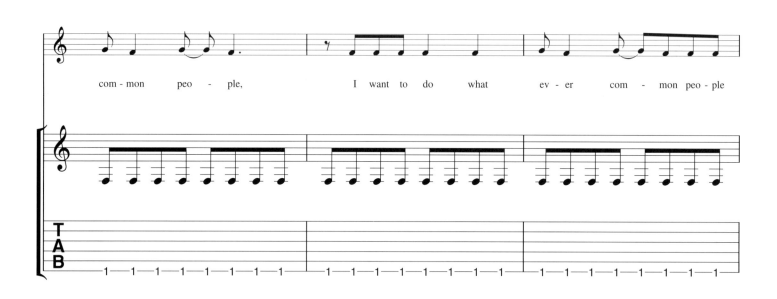

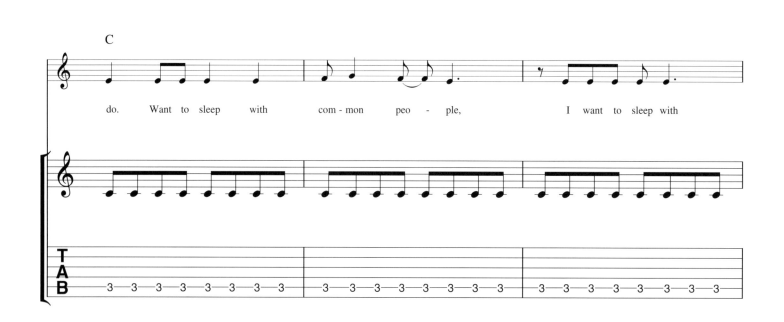

com - mon peo - ple like you._____ (Well) what else_____ could I do?__

(2° open out)

1.

I said I'll, I'll see what I can do.

2,3.

hand. Rent a flat_____ a - bove_____ a shop,__

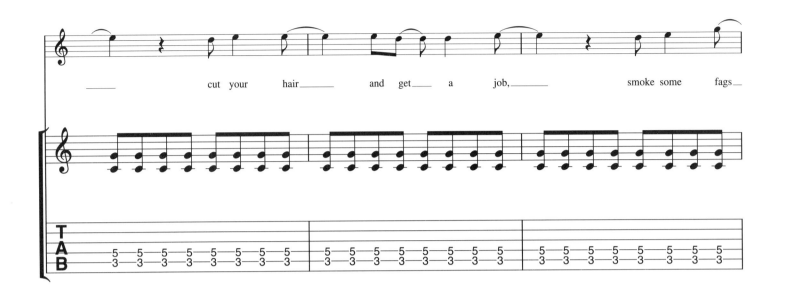

cut your   hair_____   and get____   a   job,_____   smoke some   fags__

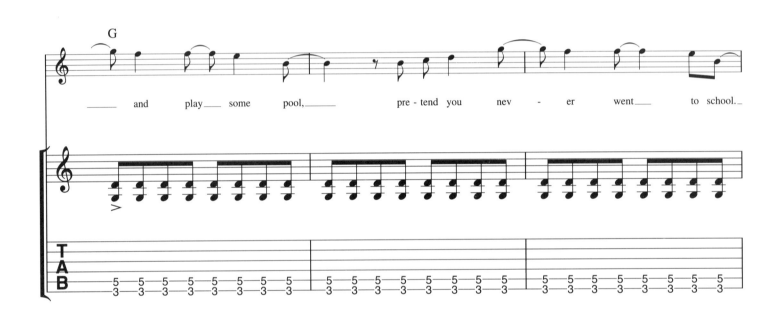

G

_____   and   play____ some   pool,_____   pre - tend you   nev - er   went____   to school.__

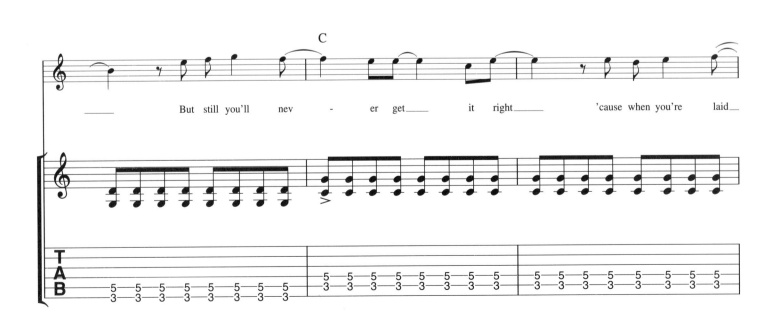

C

_____   But still you'll   nev - er   get____   it   right_____   'cause when you're   laid__

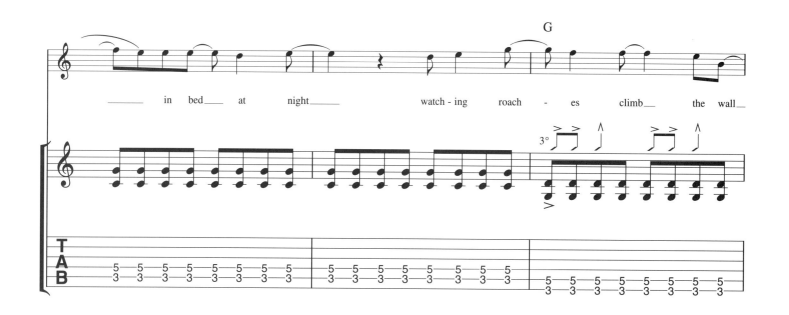

_____ in bed___ at night_____ watch - ing roach - es climb___ the wall_____

_____ if you called___ your dad___ he could stop___ it all___ yeah.

Chorus

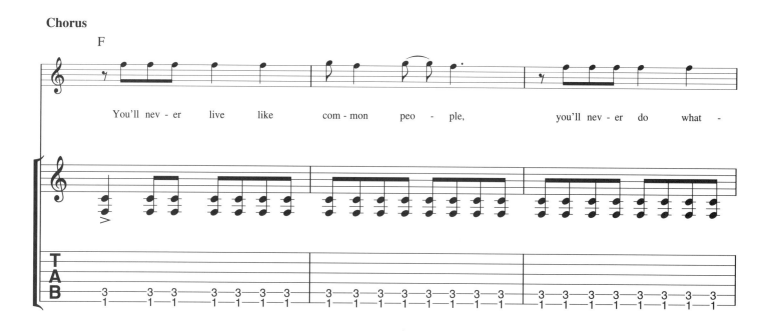

You'll nev - er live like com - mon peo - ple, you'll nev - er do what -

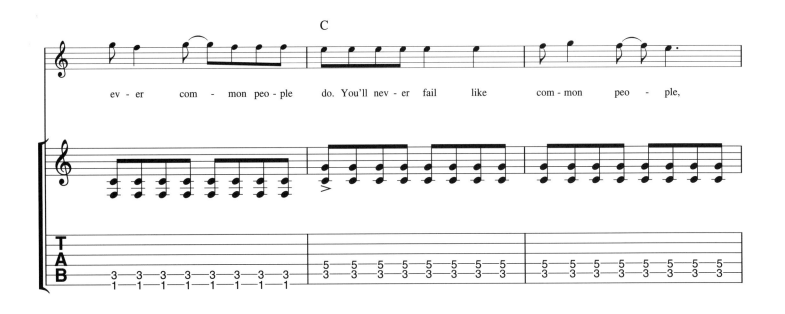

ev - er com - mon peo - ple do. You'll nev - er fail like com - mon peo - ple,

you'll nev - er watch your life_____ slide out of view,_____ and then dance__

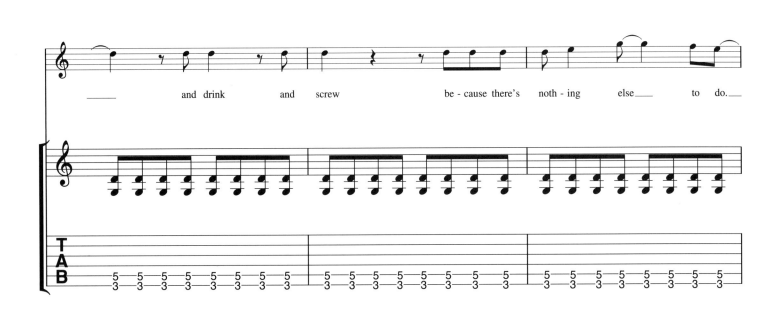

____ and drink and screw be - cause there's noth - ing else____ to do.__

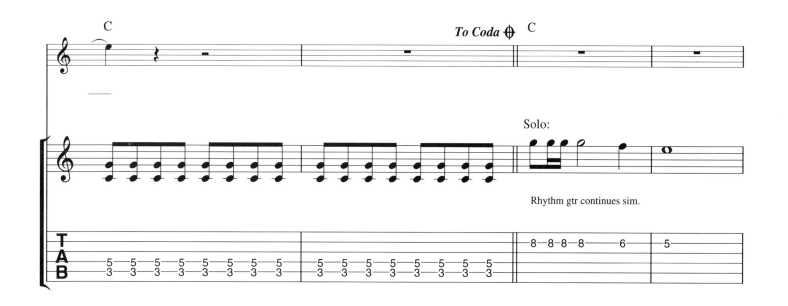

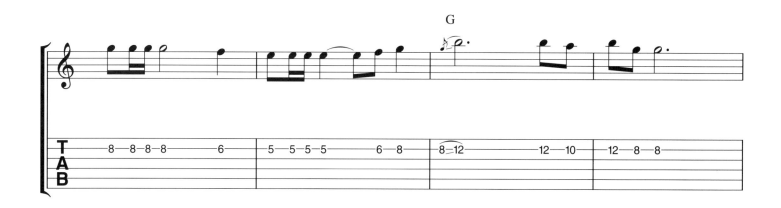

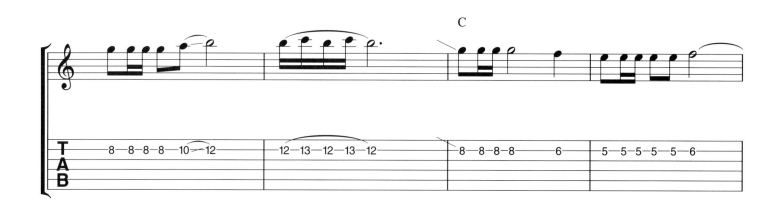

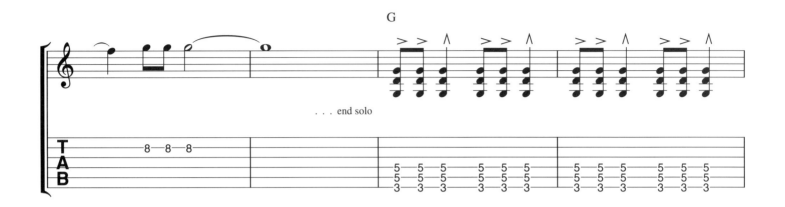

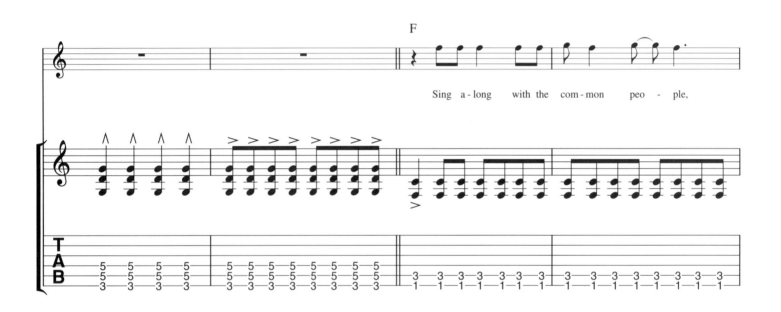

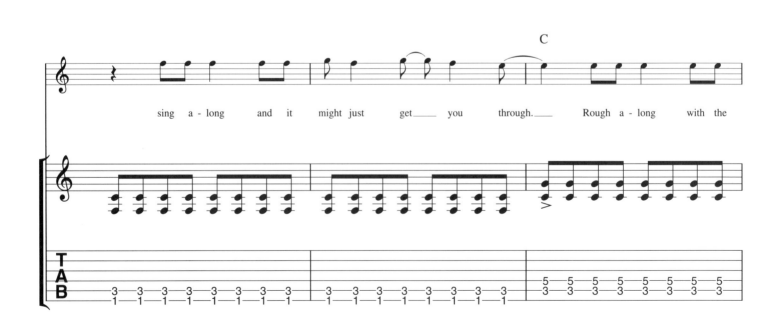

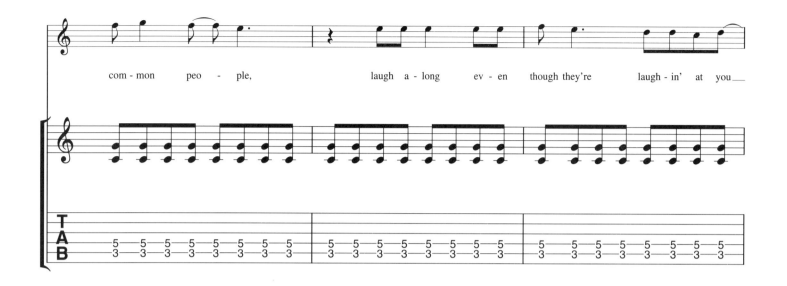

com - mon   peo - ple,   laugh a - long   ev - en   though they're   laugh - in' at you___

___   and the   stu - pid   things___ that you do_____   be - cause you   think___

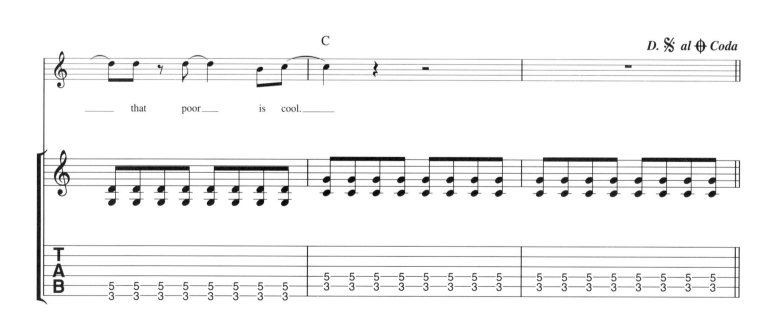

D. % al ⊕ Coda

___   that   poor___   is   cool.___

Verse 2:

I took her to a supermarket, I don't know why
But I had to start it somewhere - so it started there
I said pretend you've got no money
She laughed and said oh you're so funny - I said yeah?
Well I can't see anyone else smiling in here
Are you sure you want to live like common people?
You want to see whatever common people see
You want to sleep with common people
You want to sleep with common people like me
But she didn't understand
She just smiled and held my hand.

Verse 3 (%)

Like a dog lying in the corner, they will bite you and never warn you
Look out - they'll tear your insides out
'Cause everybody hates a tourist
Especially one who thinks it's all such a laugh
And the chip stains and grease will come out in the bath.
You will never understand
How it feels to live your life
With no meaning or control
And with nowhere left to go
You're amazed that they exist
And they burn so bright whilst you can only wonder why.

everything must go

Music by James Dean Bradfield & Sean Moore. Lyrics by Nicky Wire

Intro

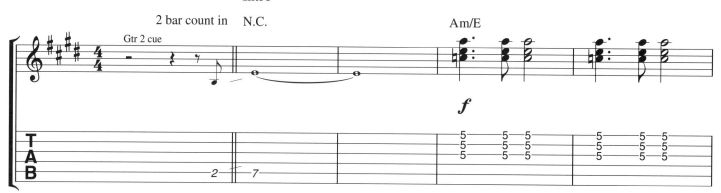

Verse

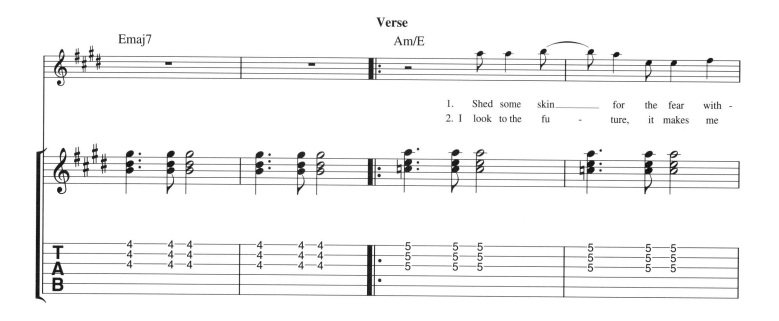

1. Shed some skin_____ for the fear with-
2. I look to the fu - ture, it makes me

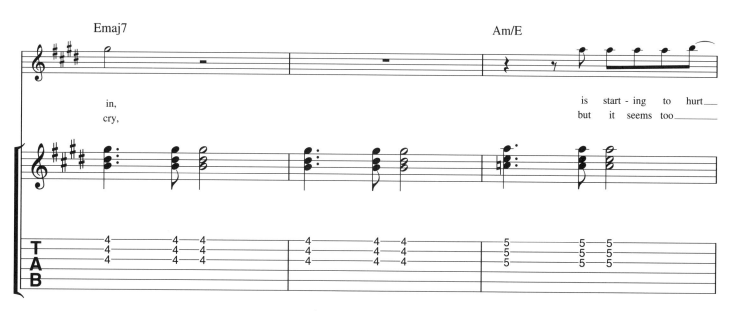

in,
cry,

is start - ing to hurt__
but it seems too_____

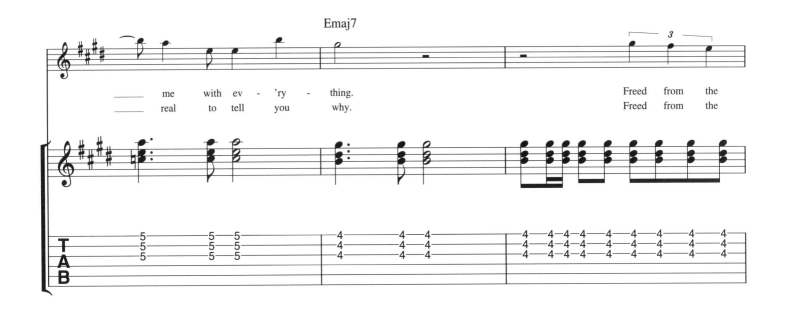

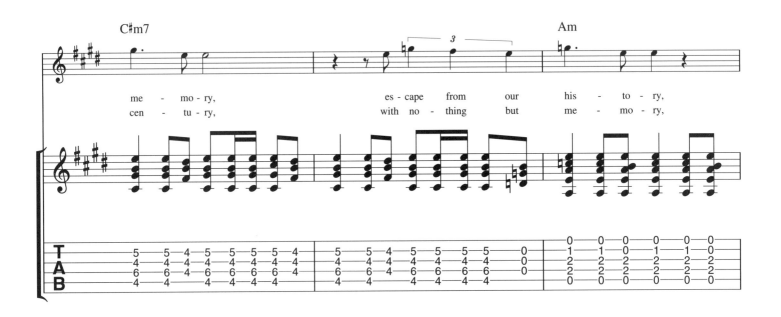

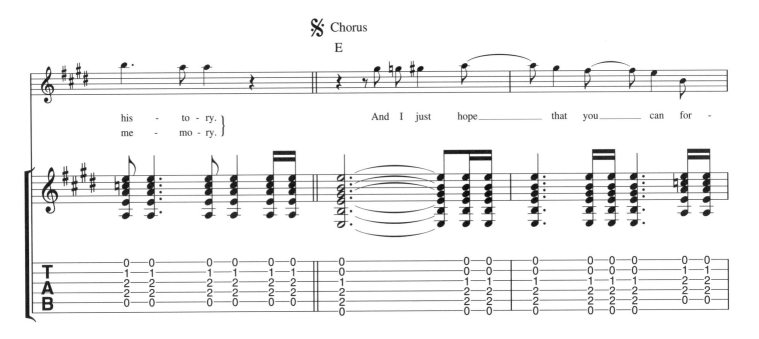

give _____ us,   but ev -

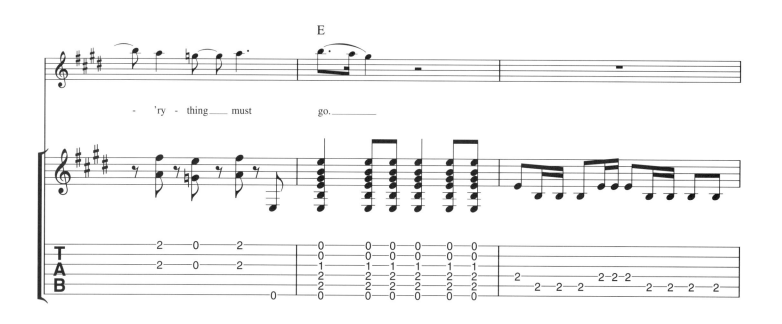

- 'ry - thing ___ must   go. ___

And if you need _____ an ex - pla - na - tion,

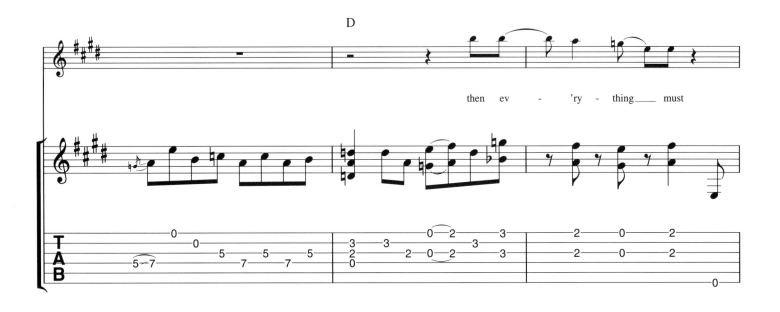

then ev - 'ry - thing____ must

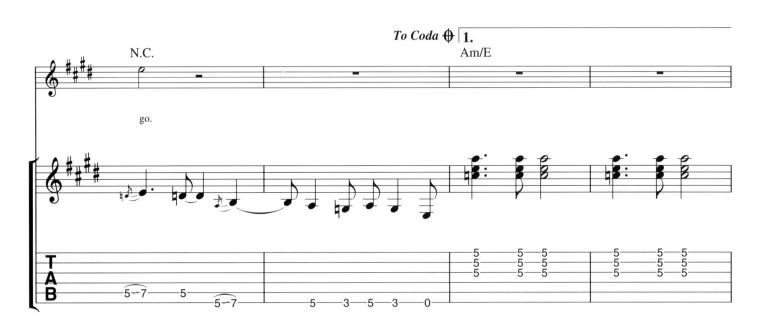

go.

To Coda ⊕ |**1.**

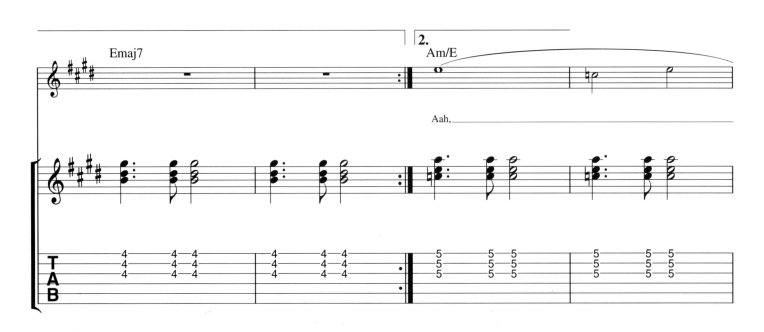

Aah,____

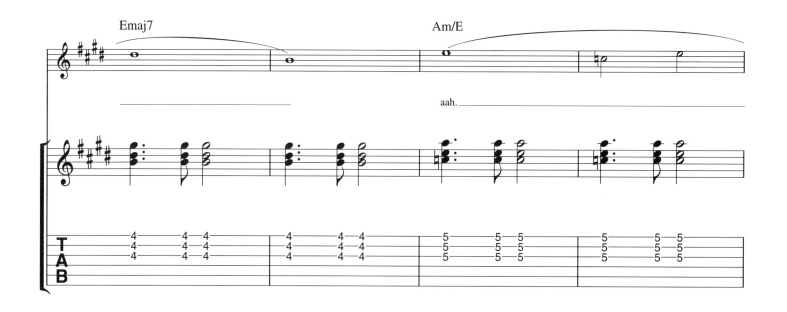

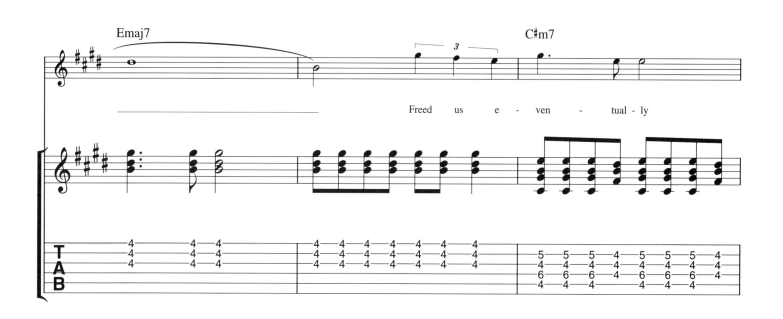

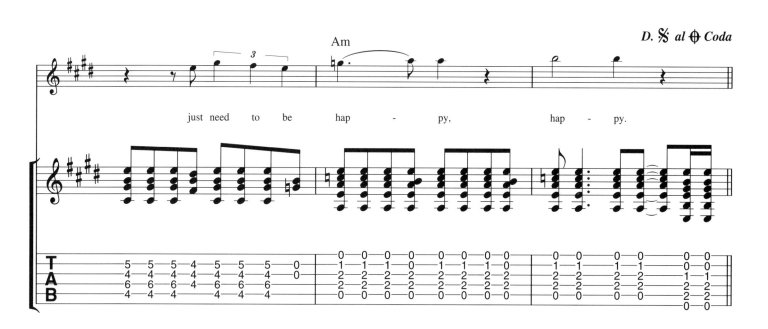

Coda ⊕

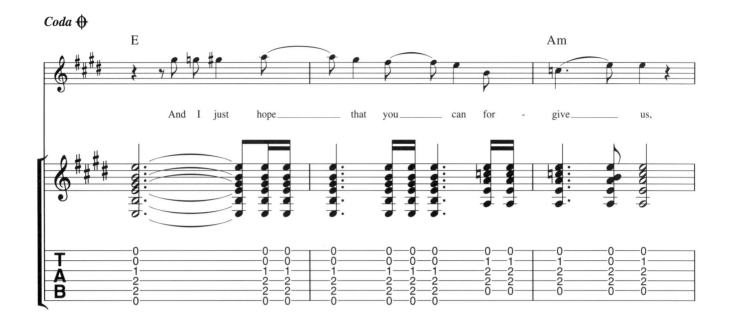

And I just hope_____ that you_____ can for - give_____ us,

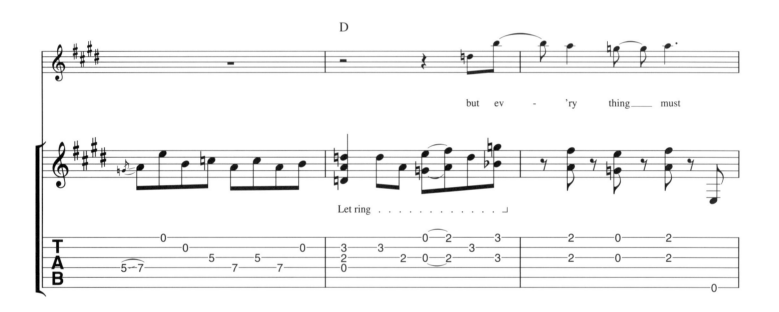

but ev - 'ry thing_____ must

Let ring . . . . ⌐

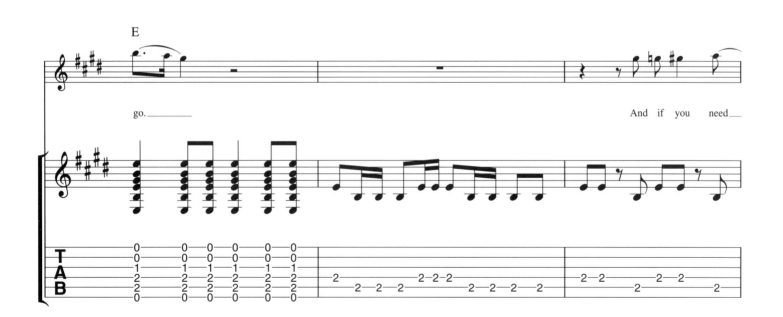

go._____

And if you need_____

an ex - pla - na - tion, 'a - tion

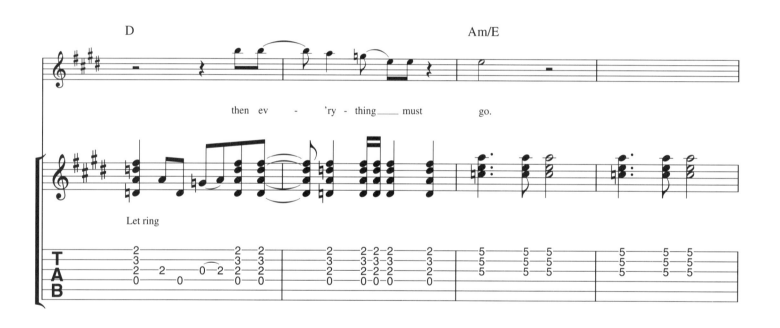

then ev - 'ry - thing____ must____ go.

Let ring

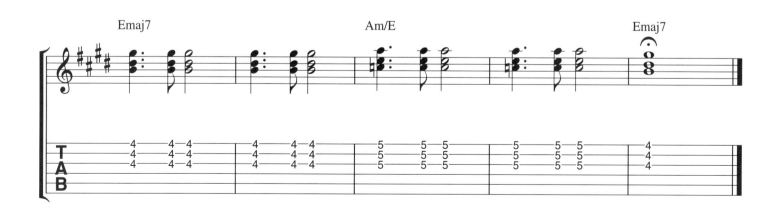

enter sandman

Words & Music by James Hetfield, Lars Ulrich & Kirk Hammett

Verse

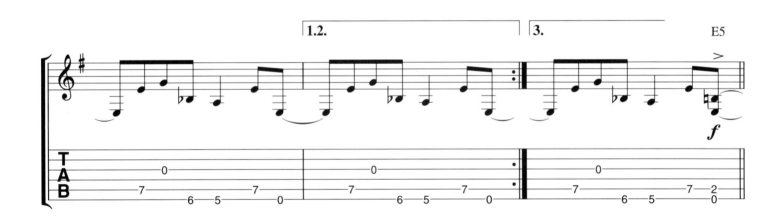

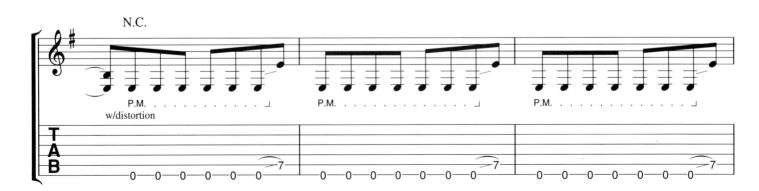

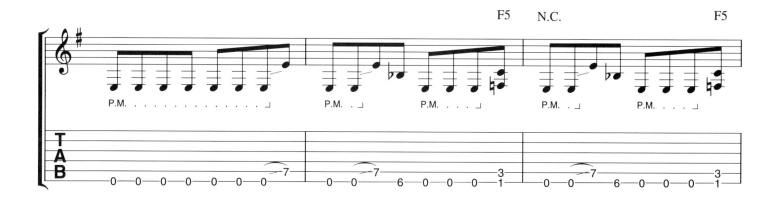

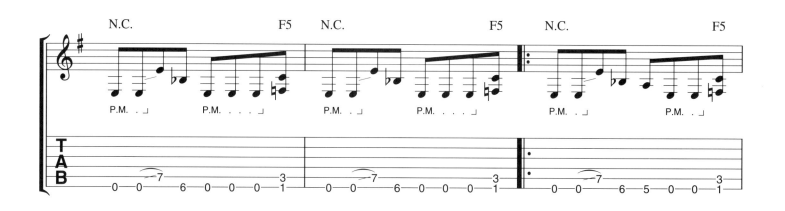

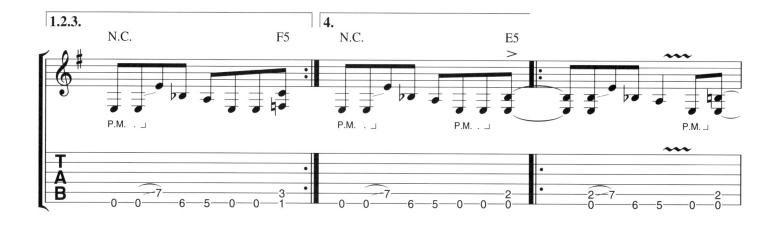

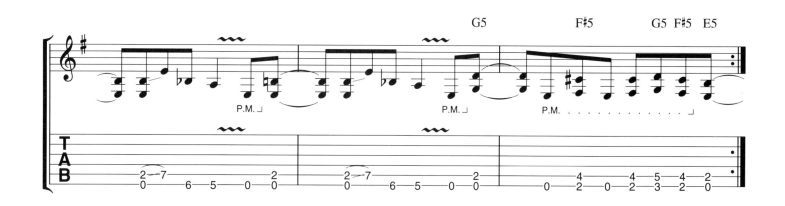

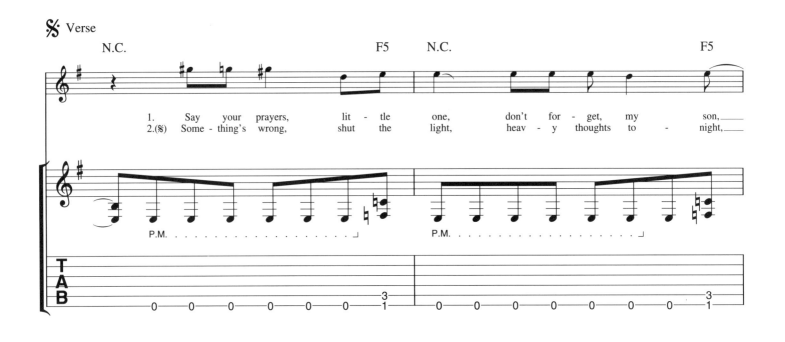

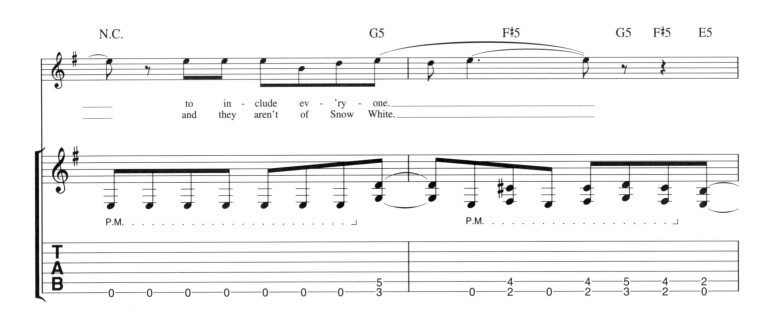

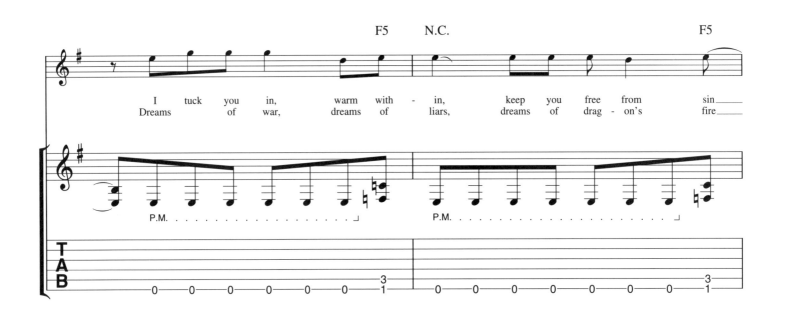

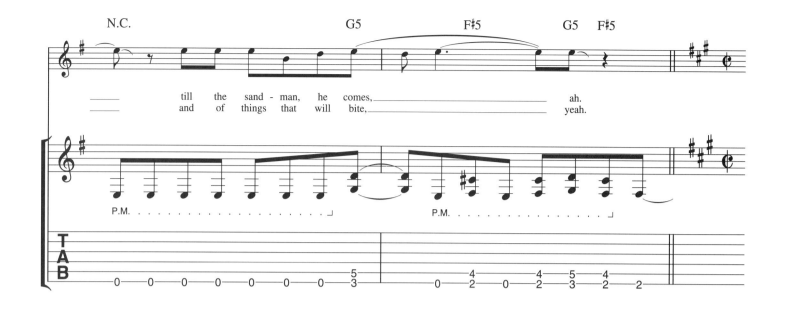

till the sand - man, he comes,_____ ah.
and of things that will bite,_____ yeah.

Pre-chorus

Sleep with one_____ eye o - pen, grip - ping your pil -

Chorus

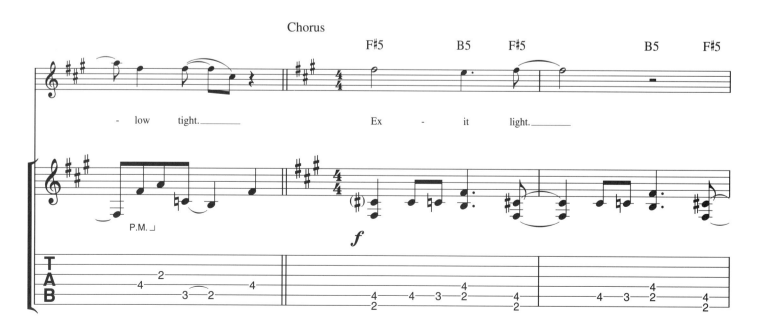

- low tight._____ Ex - it light._____

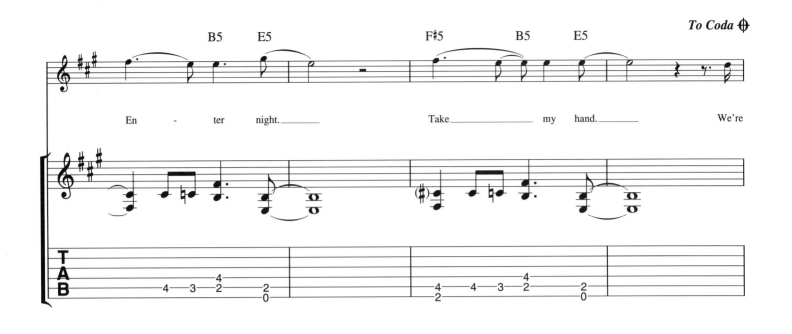

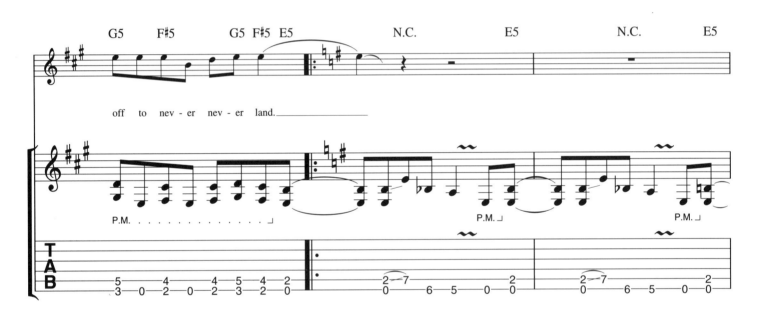

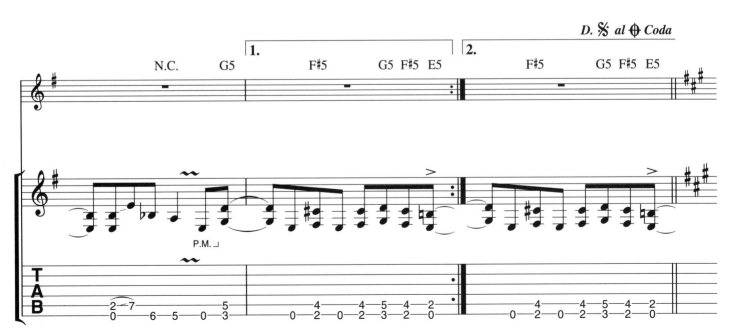

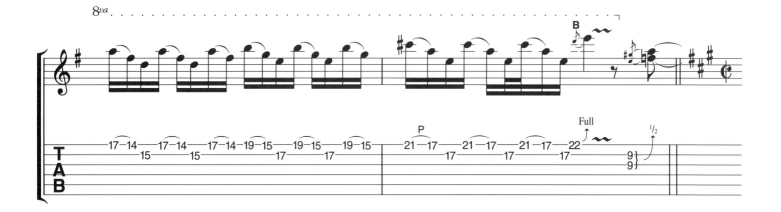

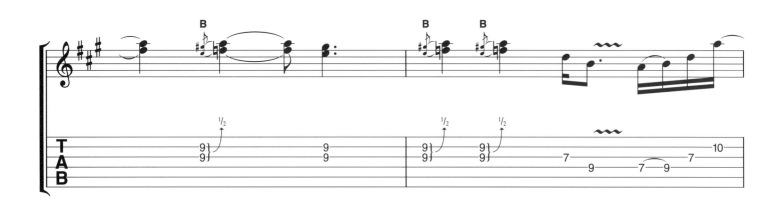

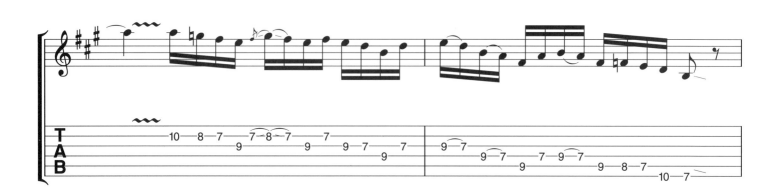

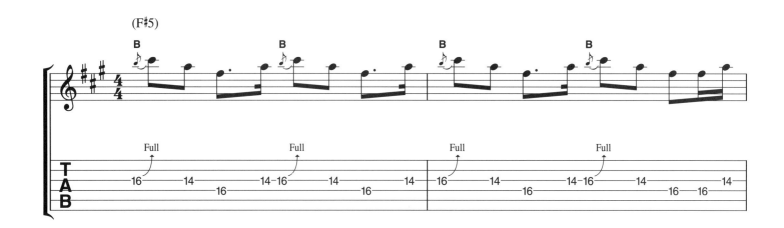

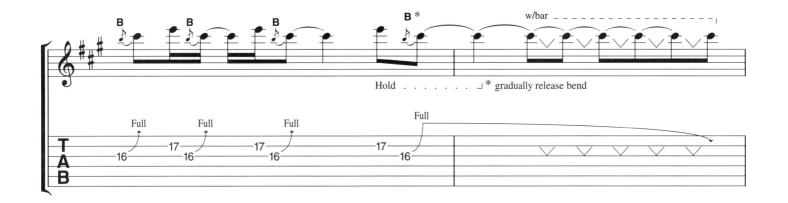

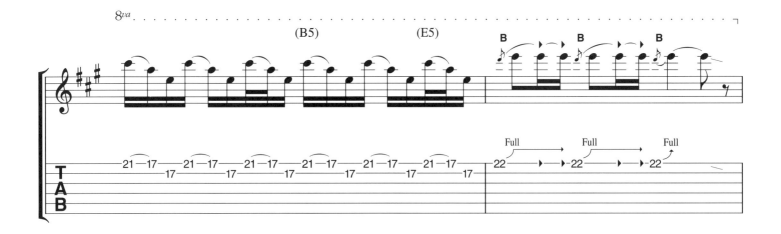

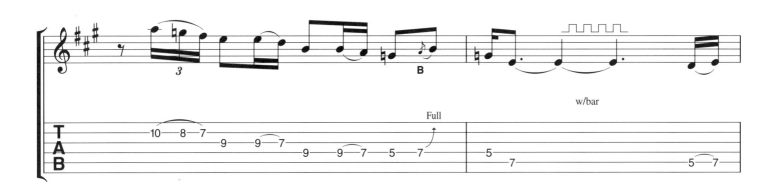

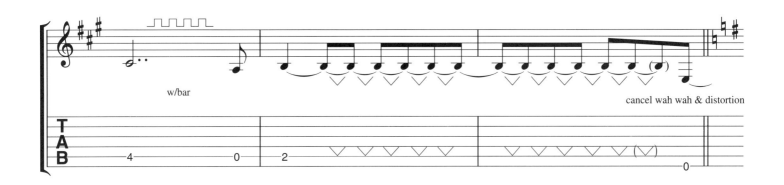

Spoken: 1. Now I lay me down to sleep.　　(Now I lay me down to sleep.)　　Pray the Lord my soul to keep.
　　I die before I wake,　　　　　　　　(If I die before I wake)　　　　Pray the Lord my soul to take.

mp w/chorus

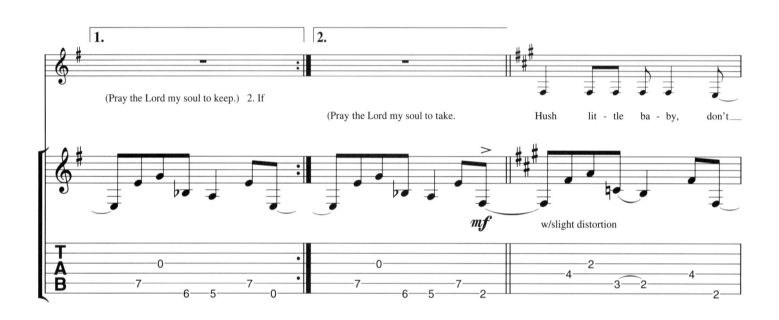

1.　　(Pray the Lord my soul to keep.)　2. If

2.　　(Pray the Lord my soul to take.　　　Hush　lit - tle　ba - by,　don't__

mf w/slight distortion

_____ say　a　word._____　　　And　nev - er　mind　that　noise　you　heard,__

play guitar with...
all these

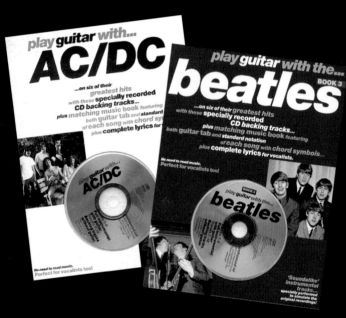

top bands and artists

play guitar with... **oasis**
...on seven of their greatest hits with these specially recorded CD backing tracks... plus matching music book featuring both guitar tab and standard notation of each song with chord symbols... plus complete lyrics for vocalists.

Seven great songs from 'Definitely Maybe' and 'What's The Story' (Morning Glory)'

No need to read music. Perfect for vocalists too!

play guitar with... **the stone roses** BOOK 2
...on six of their greatest hits with these specially recorded CD backing tracks... plus matching music book featuring both guitar tab and standard notation of each song with chord symbols... plus complete lyrics for vocalists

'Soundalike' instrumental tracks... specially performed to simulate the original recordings

play guitar with... **paul weller**
...on eight of his greatest hits with these specially recorded CD backing tracks... plus matching music book featuring both guitar tab and standard notation of each song with chord symbols... plus complete lyrics for vocalists.

'Soundalike' instrumental tracks... specially performed to simulate the original recordings.

No need to read music. Perfect for vocalists too!

play guitar with... **the 70's**
...on eight great hits from ac/dc, derek and the dominoes, dire straits, the eagles, free, slade, thin lizzy and wings with these specially recorded CD backing tracks... plus matching music book featuring both guitar tab and standard notation of each song with chord symbols... plus complete lyrics for vocalists

'Soundalike' instrumental tracks... specially performed to simulate the original recordings

play guitar with... **the 90's**
...on seven great hits from eric clapton, manic street preachers, metallica, alanis morissette, oasis, pulp and the seahorses with these specially recorded CD backing tracks... plus matching music book featuring both guitar tab and standard notation of each song with chord symbols... plus complete lyrics for vocalists

'Soundalike' instrumental tracks... specially performed to simulate the original recordings

No need to read music. Perfect for vocalists too!

bob marley
includes:
i shot the sheriff
jamming
no woman, no cry
Order No. AM937739

metallica
includes:
enter sandman
fade to black
the unforgiven
Order No. AM92559

metallica book 2
includes:
creeping death
seek and destroy
whiskey in the jar
Order No. AM955977

alanis morissette
includes:
hand in my pocket
ironic
you oughta know
Order No. AM943723

oasis
includes:
cigarettes & alcohol
morning glory
supersonic
Order No. AM935330

ocean colour scene
includes:
the circle
the day we caught the train
the riverboat song
Order No. AM943712

elvis presley
includes:
all shook up
blue suede shoes
hound dog
Order No. AM937090

pulp
includes:
common people
disco 2000
sorted for e's & wizz
Order No. AM938124

the rolling stones
includes:
brown sugar
(i can't get no) satisfaction
jumpin' jack flash
Order No. AM90247

sting
includes:
an englishman in
  new york
fields of gold
if you love somebody
  set them free
Order No. AM928092

the stone roses
includes:
i am the resurrection
i wanna be adored
ten storey love song
Order No. AM943701

the stone roses book 2
includes:
fool's gold
love spreads
one love
Order No. AM955890

suede
includes:
animal nitrate
electricity
we are the pigs
Order No. AM955955

paul weller
includes:
the changingman
out of the sinking
wild wood
Order No. AM937827

the who
includes:
i can see for miles
pinball wizard
substitute
Order No. AM955867

the 60's
includes:
all along the watchtower
  (jimi hendrix)
born to be wild
  (steppenwolf)
not fade away
  (the rolling stones)
Order No. AM957748

the 70's
includes:
all right now (free)
hotel california
  (the eagles)
live and let die (wings)
Order No. AM957759

the 80's
includes:
addicted to love
  (robert palmer)
need you tonight (inxs)
where the streets have
  no name (U2)
Order No. AM957760

the 90's
includes:
everything must go
  (manic street preachers)
love is the law (the seahorses)
wonderwall (oasis)
Order No. AM957770

play guitar with...
sample the whole series with these special compilations...

the gold book
play guitar with...
...on eight great hits from **dire straits, the beatles, chuck berry, elvis presley, the kinks, eric clapton, john lennon** and **john lee hooker**
with these **specially recorded** CD backing tracks...
plus **matching music book** featuring both **guitar tab** and **standard notation** of each song with **chord symbols** complete **lyrics** for vocalists
'Soundalike' instrumental tracks... specially performed to simulate the original recordings

the platinum book
play guitar with...
...on seven great hits from **kula shaker, manic street preachers, ocean colour scene, oasis, stone roses, pulp** and **paul weller**
with these **specially recorded** CD backing tracks...
plus **matching music book** featuring both **guitar tab** and **standard notation** of each song with **chord symbols...** plus **complete lyrics** for vocalists
'Soundalike' instrumental tracks... specially performed to simulate the original recordings

play guitar with... the **platinum** book
Full instrumental with guitar Tracks 8-14 Backing tracks without guitar
Enhanced CD

No need to read music. Perfect for vocalists too!

the gold book
includes eight classic tracks:
jailhouse rock (elvis presley)
johnny b. goode (chuck berry)
layla (eric clapton)
sultans of swing (dire straits)
the healer (john lee hooker)
ticket to ride (the beatles)
woman (john lennon)
you really got me (the kinks)
Order No. AM951907

the platinum book
includes seven great songs:
a design for life
  (manic street preachers)
cigarettes & alcohol (oasis)
disco 2000 (pulp)
elephant stone (stone roses)
govinda (kula shaker)
the changingman (paul weller)
the riverboat song
  (ocean colour scene)
Order No. AM951918

Arthur Dick *has transcribed the music and provided the recorded guitar parts for most of the titles in the* **play guitar with...** *series, often bringing in other professional specialist musicians to achieve the most authentic sounds possible!*

A session guitarist with over twenty years' experience, he has worked with Cliff Richard, Barbara Dickson, Helen Shapiro, Bernie Flint and Chris Rea among others.

Arthur has played in many West End stage shows, and is in regular demand as a session player for TV, radio, and advertising productions.

He currently lectures on jazz and contemporary guitar at University Goldsmith's College, and works as a freelance production consultant.

Available from all good music retailers or, in case of difficulty, contact:

Music Sales Limited
Newmarket Road,
Bury St. Edmunds,
Suffolk IP33 3YB.
telephone 01284 725725
fax 01284 702592

www.musicsales.com

PUB04634

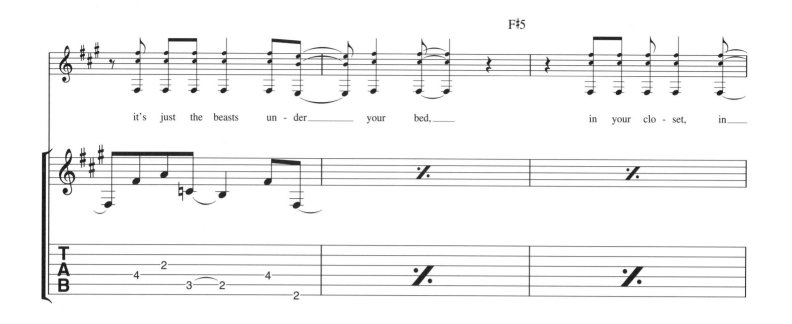

it's just the beasts un-der _____ your bed, _____ in your clo-set, in _____

_____ your head. _____ Ex - it light. _____ En - ter night. _____

Chorus

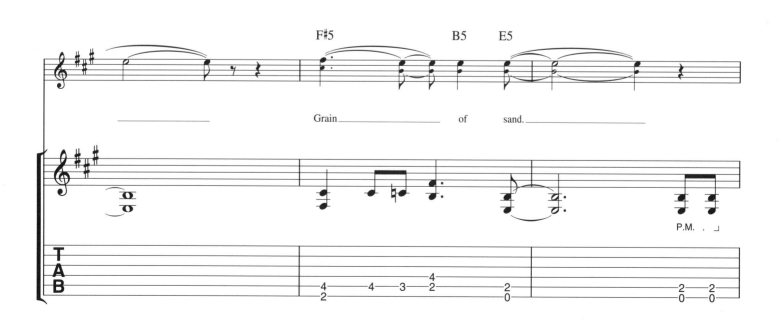

Grain _____ of sand. _____

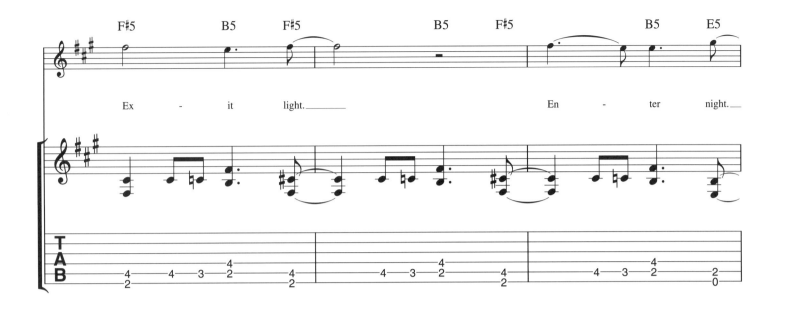

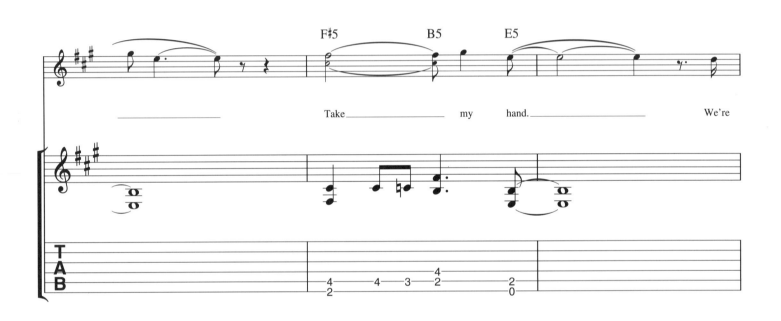

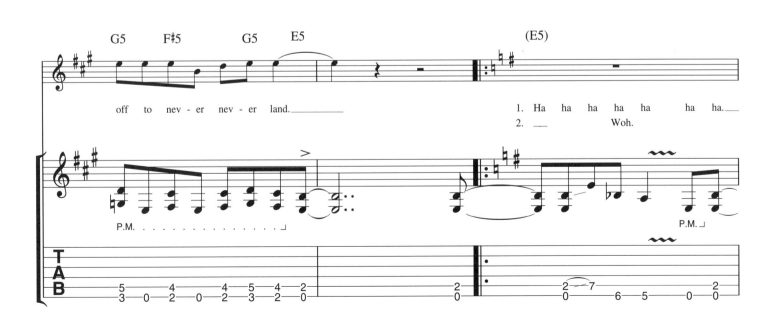

Ooh.   Yeah, yeah!   Yo, ___

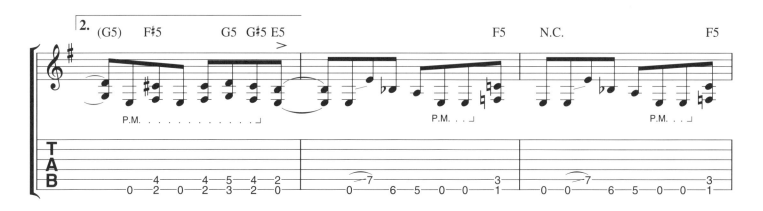

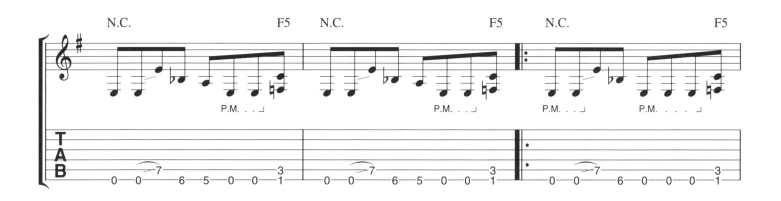

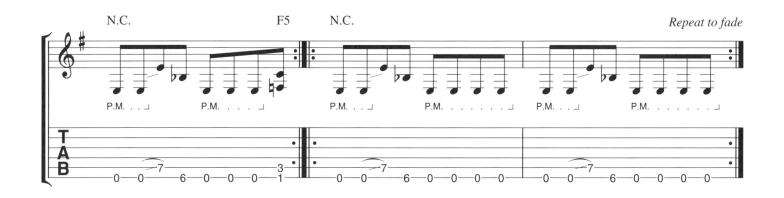

hand in my pocket

Music by Alanis Morissette & Glenn Ballard. Words by Alanis Morissette

Intro

2 bar count in:

Verse

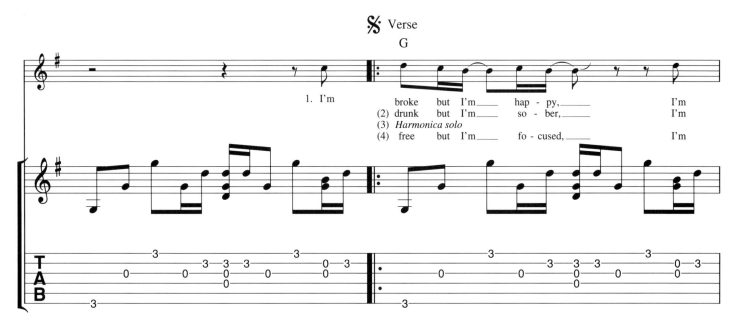

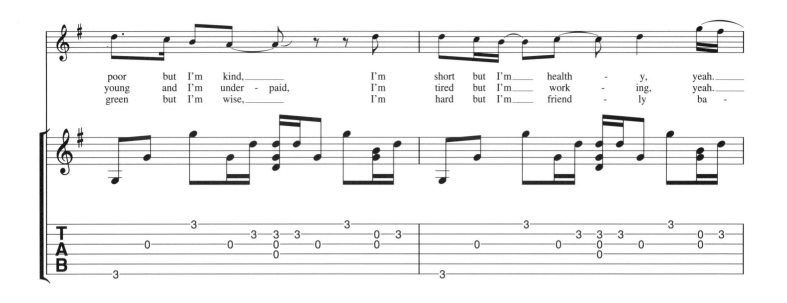

poor but I'm kind,_____ I'm short but I'm_____ health - y, yeah._____
young and I'm under - paid, I'm tired but I'm_____ work - ing, yeah._____
green but I'm wise,_____ I'm hard but I'm_____ friend - ly ba -

_____ I'm_____ high but I'm ground - ed, I'm_____
_____ I_____ care but I'm rest - less, I'm_____
by. I'm_____ sad but I'm laugh - ing. I'm_____

sane but I'm o - ver - whelmed, I'm lost but I'm hope - ful, ba -
here but I'm real - ly_____ gone, I'm wrong and I'm sor - ry ba -
brave but I'm chick - en_____ shit, I'm sick but I'm pret - ty ba -

Chorus
G5/F

- by. }
- by. } And   what   it   all   comes down _____ to
- by. }

Csus2   G5

is   that   ev - 'ry - thing's   gon - na   be   fine,   fine,   fine, _____
is   that   ev - 'ry - thing's   gon - na   be   quite   al -   right, _____
is   that   I   have - n't   got   it   all   fig - ured   out,   just   yet, _____
is   that   no - one's   real - ly   got   it   fig - ured   out   just   yet, _____

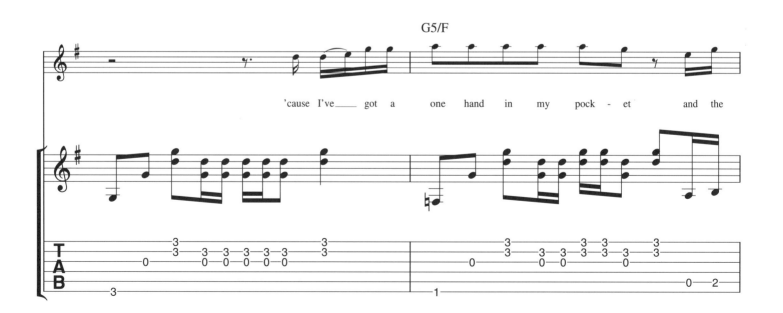

G5/F

'cause I've ___ got   a   one   hand   in   my   pock - et   and   the

oth - er one {
is giv - in' a high five.
flick - in' a cig - a - rette.
giv - in' a peace sign.
is play - in' a pian - o.

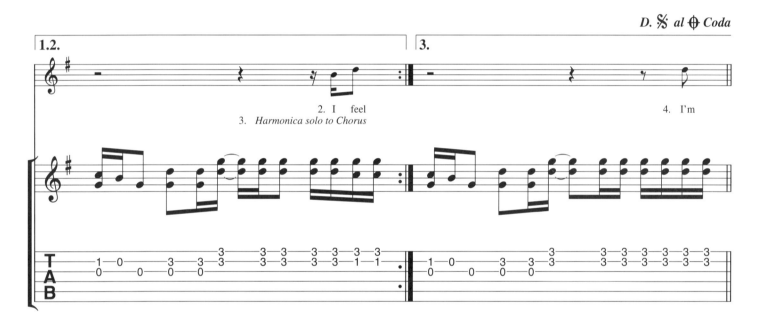

2. I feel
3. *Harmonica solo to Chorus*

4. I'm

Coda ⊕

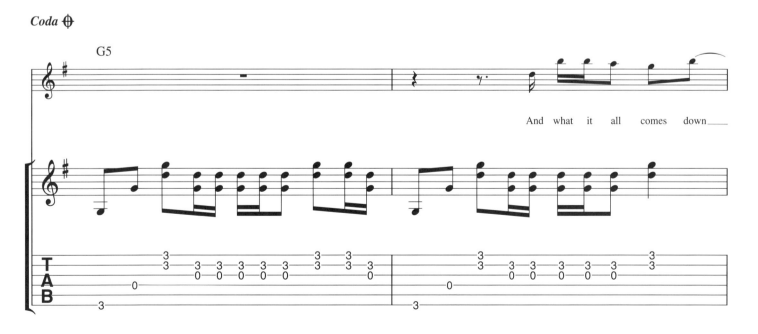

And what it all comes down___

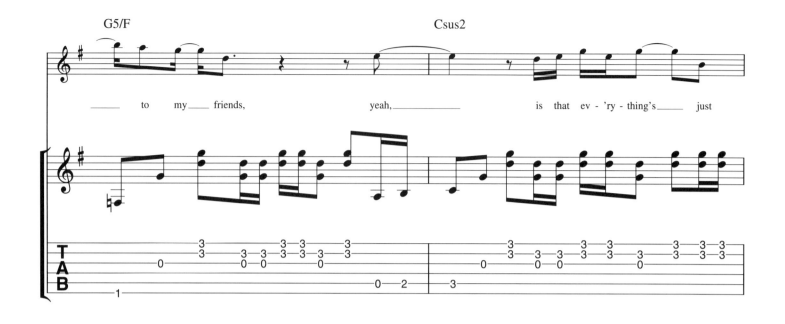

to my____ friends, yeah,_____ is that ev-'ry-thing's____ just

fine, fine,_____ fine._____ 'Cause I've___ got a

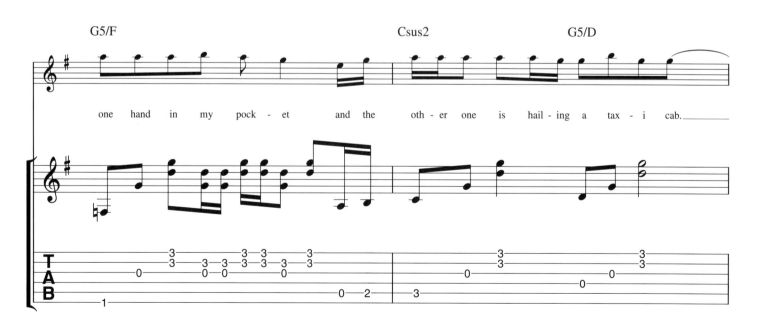

one hand in my pock-et and the oth-er one is hail-ing a tax-i cab.____

Cue harmonica:

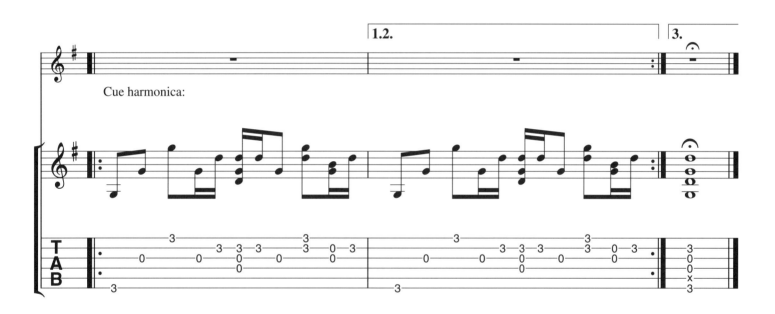

tears in heaven

Words & Music by Eric Clapton & Will Jennings

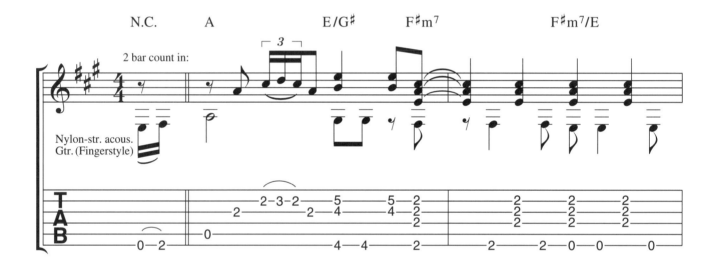

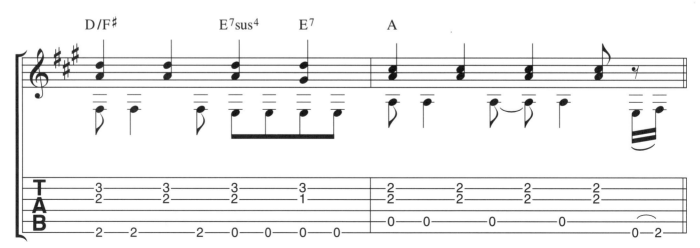

Verse

1. Would you know my name
(3x)
See Block Lyrics for Verses 2 & 3

if I saw you in hea - ven? Would it be the same

If I saw you in hea - ven?

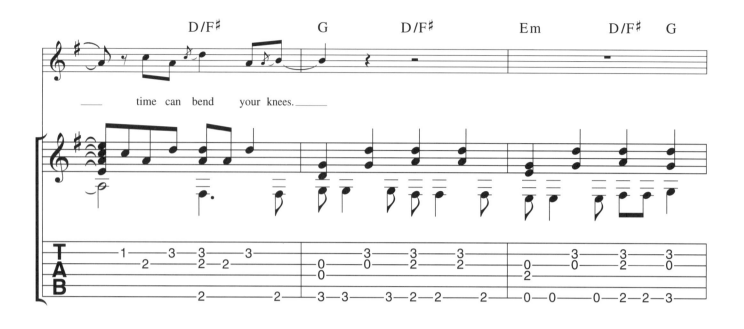

time can bend   your knees.

Time can break   your heart,_____   have ya   beg - gin' please,_____   beg - gin' please.

2nd gtr solo

46

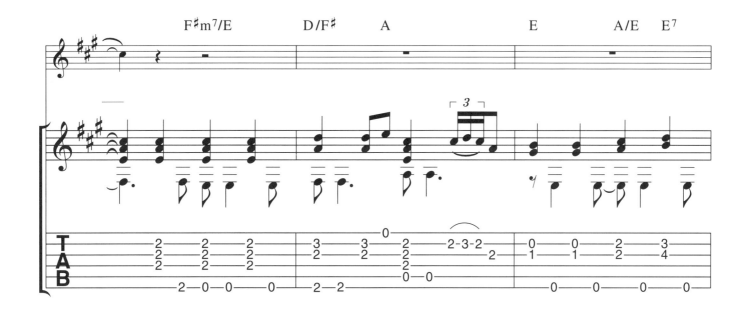

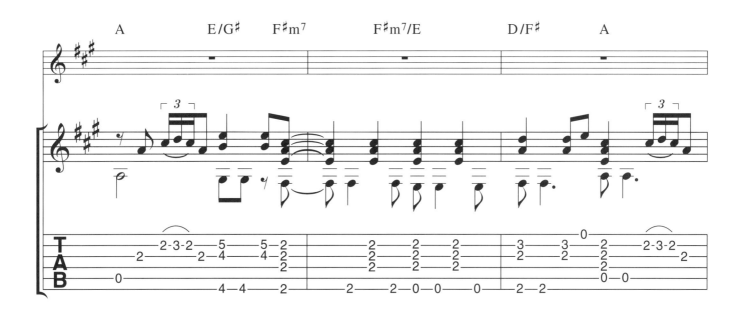

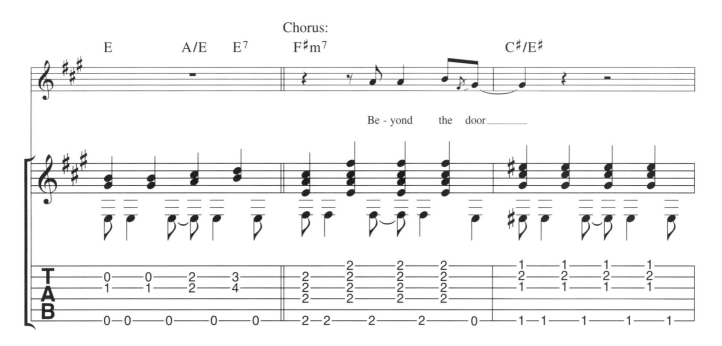

there's peace, I'm sure,_____ and I know there'll be no more_____

tears____ in hea - ven.

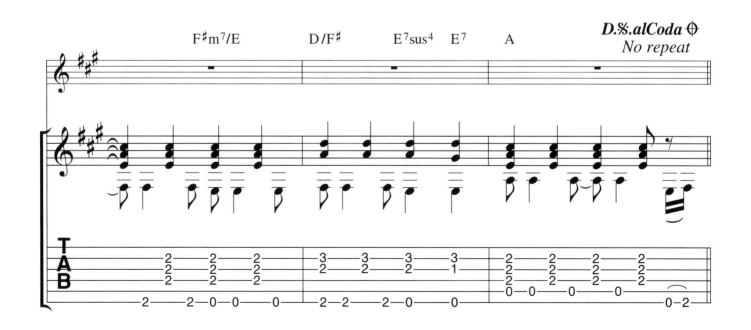

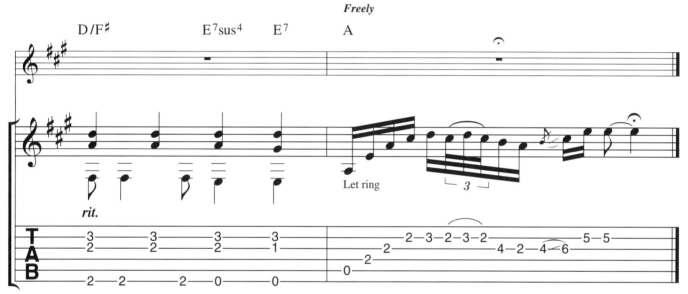

Verse 2:
Would you hold my hand
If I saw you in heaven?
Would you help me stand
If I saw you in heaven?

Chorus 2:
I'll find my way
Through night and day,
'Cause I know I just can't stay
Here in heaven.

Verse 3 (%):
Would you know my name
If I saw you in heaven?
Would you do the same
If I saw you in heaven?

Chorus 3 (%):
I must be strong
And carry on,
'Cause I know I don't belong
Here in heaven.

wonderwall

Words & Music by Noel Gallagher

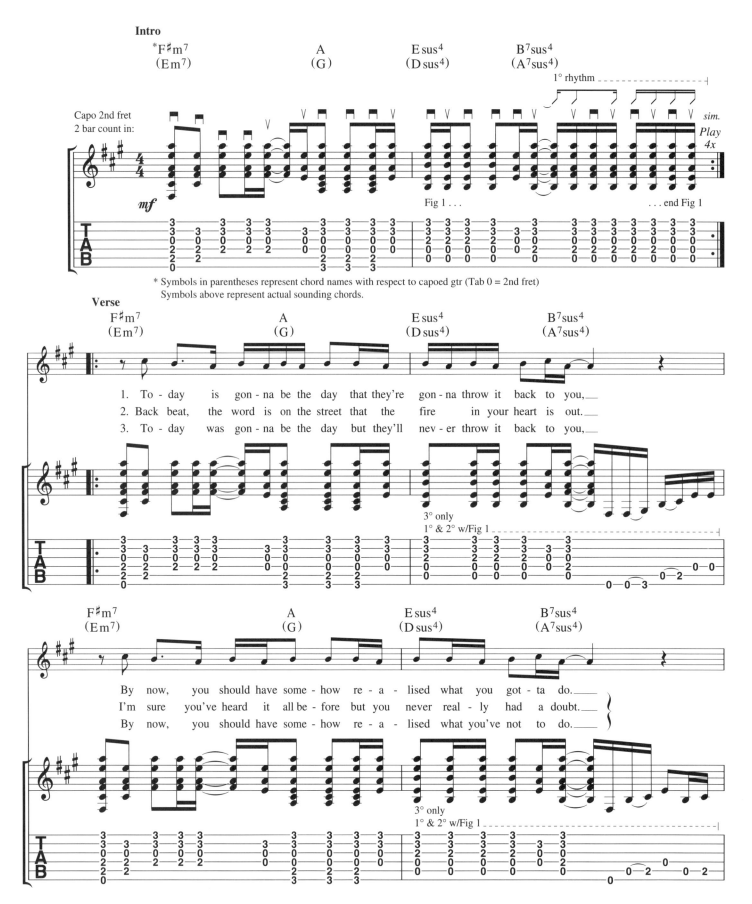

* Symbols in parentheses represent chord names with respect to capoed gtr (Tab 0 = 2nd fret)
Symbols above represent actual sounding chords.

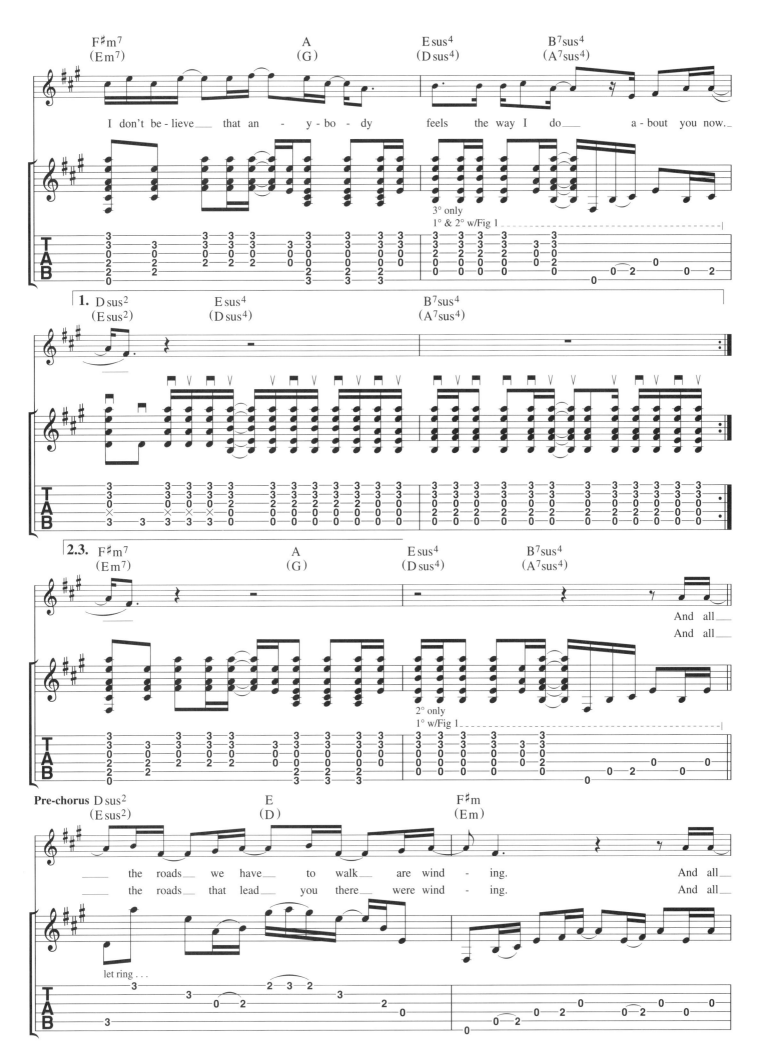

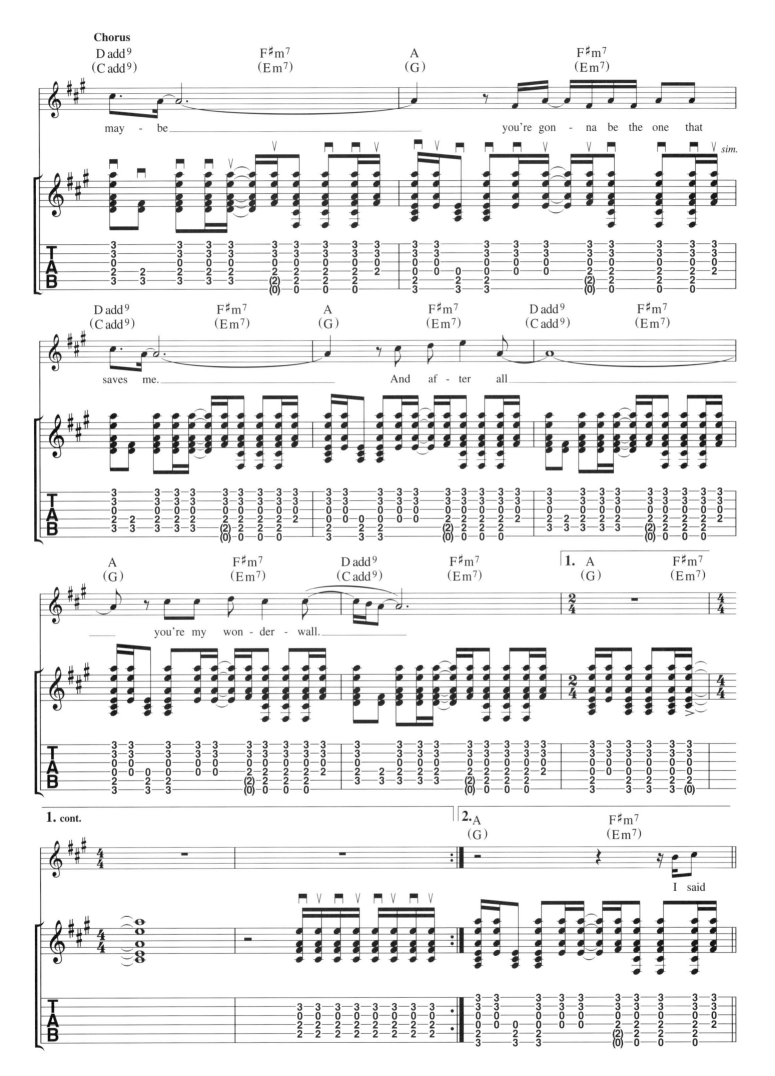

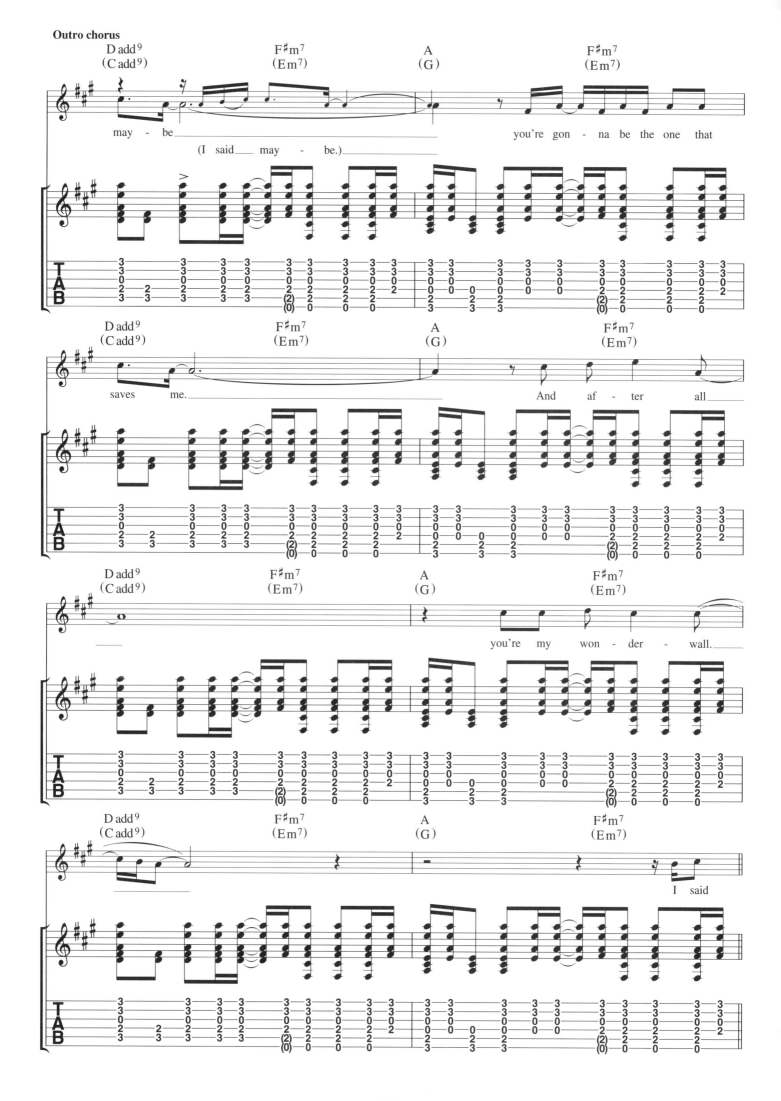

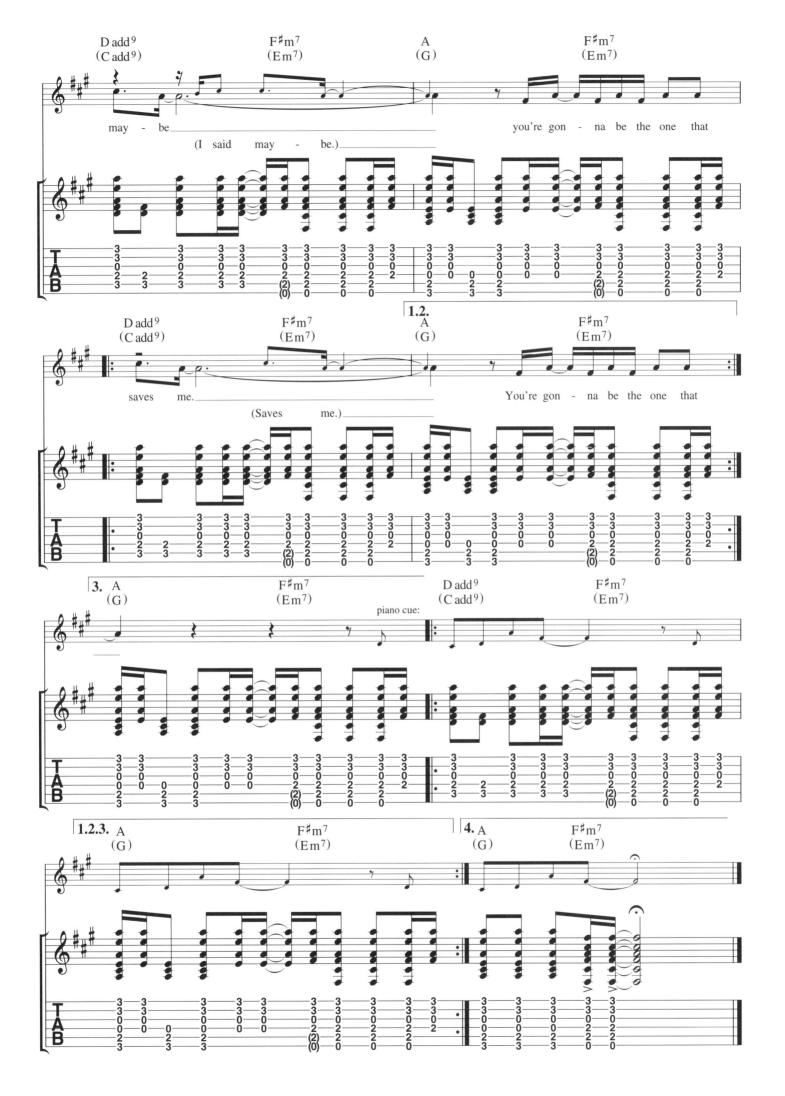

may - be _____ you're gon - na be the one that
(I said may - be.) _____

saves me. _____ You're gon - na be the one that
(Saves me.) _____

love is the law

Words & Music by John Squire

Capo 2nd fret
2 bar count in:

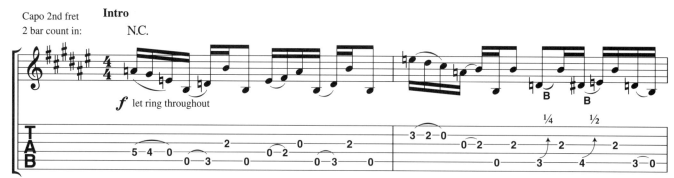

* Symbols in parentheses represent chord names with respect to capoed gtr (Tab 0 = 2nd fret)
Symbols above represent actual sounding chords.

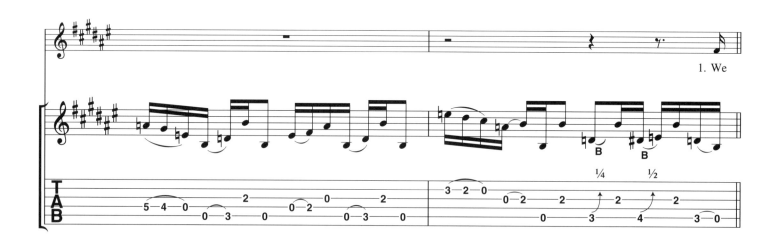

Verse

lived in a dog fish egg case, you could bare - ly call it home.____ A
2. Mad Liz - zy Crumb's blind cob - blers thumbs were a sight to be - hold. She was a
3. Strap on Sally chased us down the alley. We feared for our be - hinds. O-

* Symbols in parentheses represent chord names with respect to capoed gtr (Tab 0 = 2nd fret)
Symbols above represent actual sounding chords.

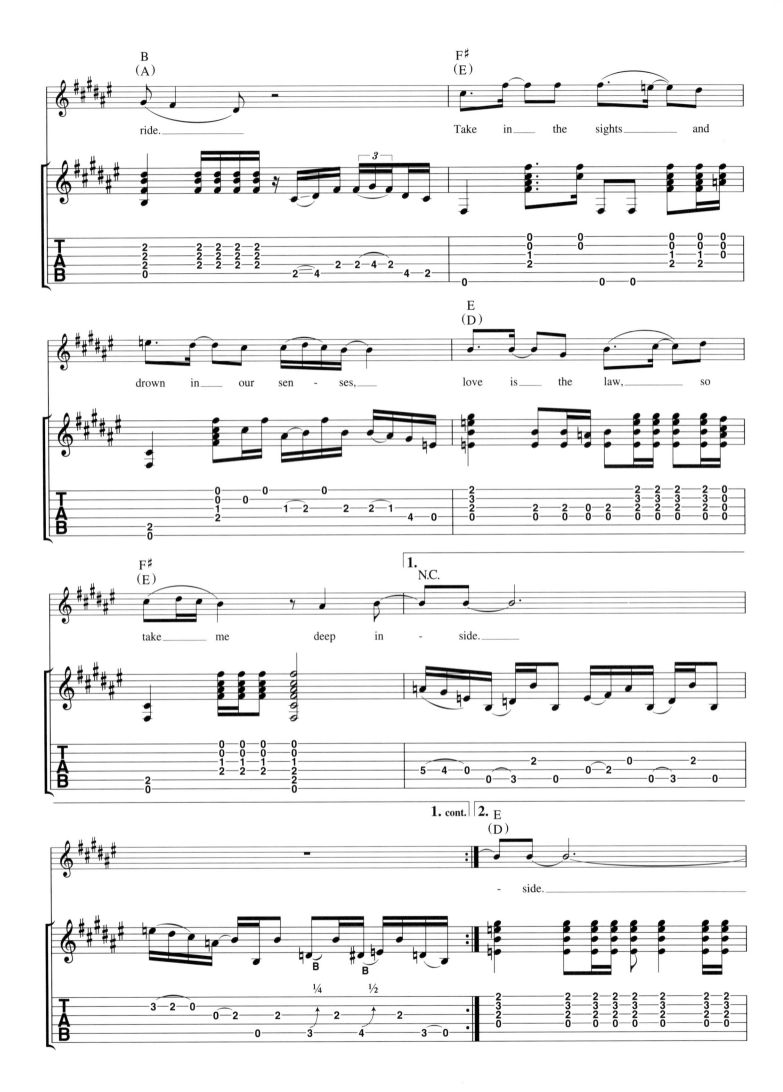

Chorus

Now we know where we're go - ing ba - by we can lay back, en - joy the ride.

Take in the sights and drown in our sen - ses,

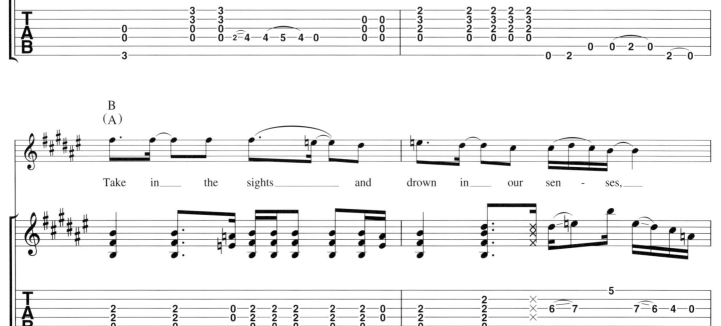

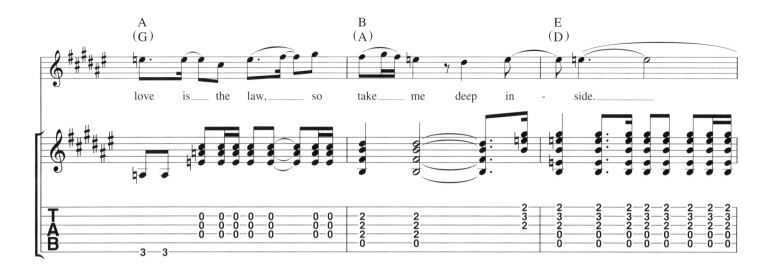

love is___ the law,___ so take___ me deep in - side.___

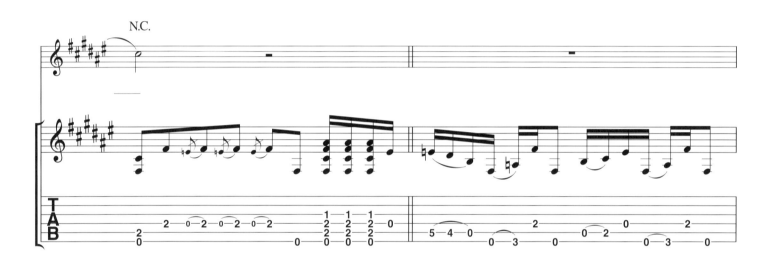

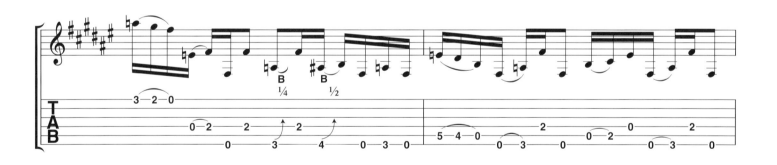

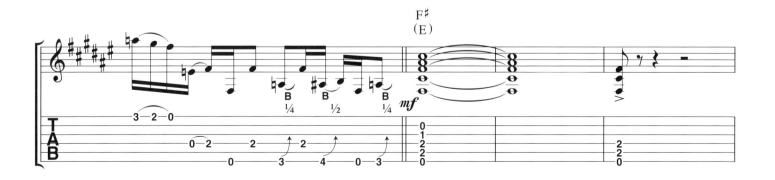

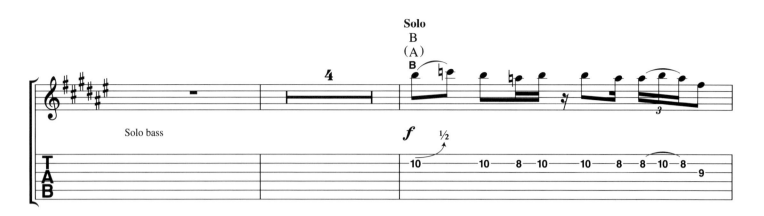

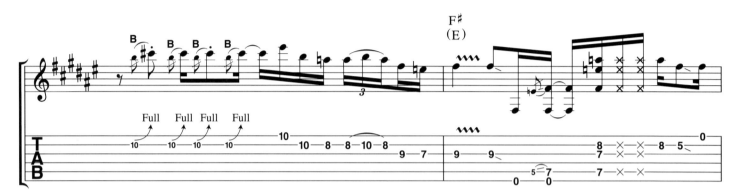

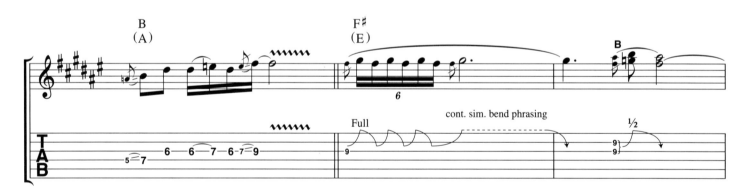

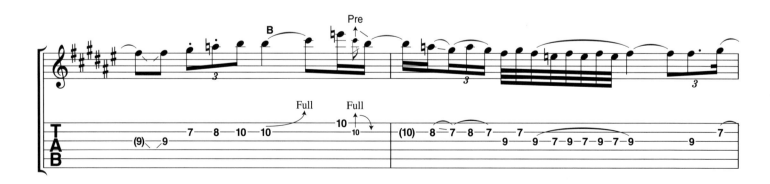

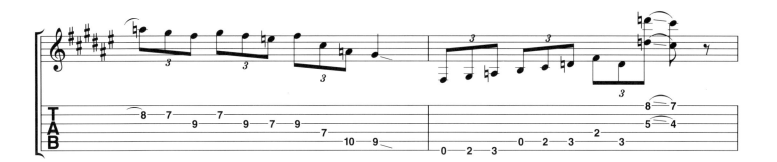
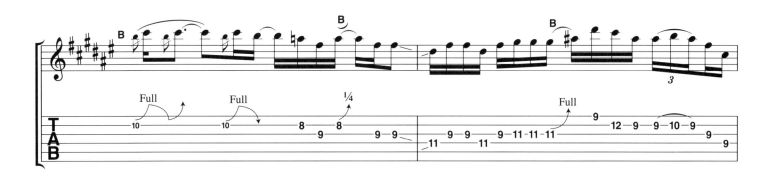
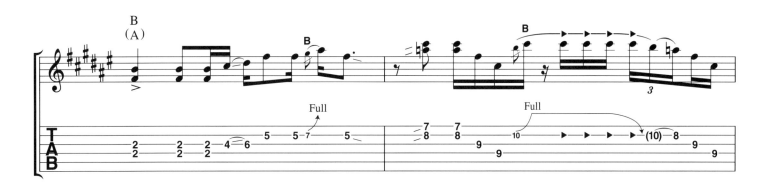
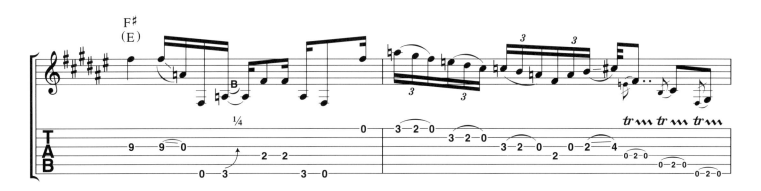
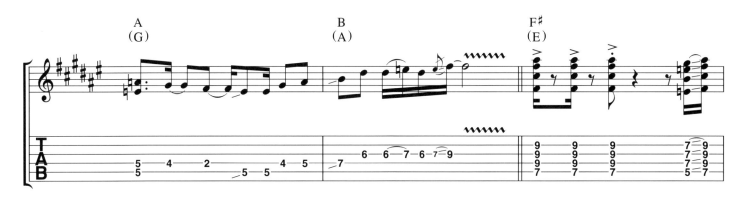

12/00 (38979)